Collectors' Coins

Pre-Decimal Issues. By Cl

C000181562

Gold Coins	1797 to 1968
Silver Coins	1800 to 1970
Copper Based Coins	1797 to 1970

39th Edition © 2012

ISBN: 978-0-948964-81-7

BRITISH NUMISMATIC TRADE ASSOCIATION BNTA *

A wealth of numismatic information and a compilation of averaged selling-prices drawn from the online Rotographic database, dealers' lists, coin auctions, numismatic magazines and experience in the trade. Special thanks to London Coins (www.londoncoins.co.uk) and Colin Cooke (www.colincooke.com) for making their price data available to the author.

The preceding 2011, 38th edition of this book was ISBN 978-0-948964-74-9.

Errors and Omissions:
Every effort has been made to ensure that the information and price data contained within this book is accurate and complete. However, errors do sometimes have a habit of creeping in unnoticed, and with this in mind the following email address has been established for notifications of omissions and errors: info@rotographic.com. Readers within the UK can also call the telephone number below.

Special thanks to everyone involved.

This book is dedicated to Amy Winehouse.

www.rotographic.com
020 308 69996

In Association with Predecimal

* This book is not endorsed or supported by the British Numismatic Trade Association, it has simply been written by one of its members. See www.bnta.net for further details on the BNTA.

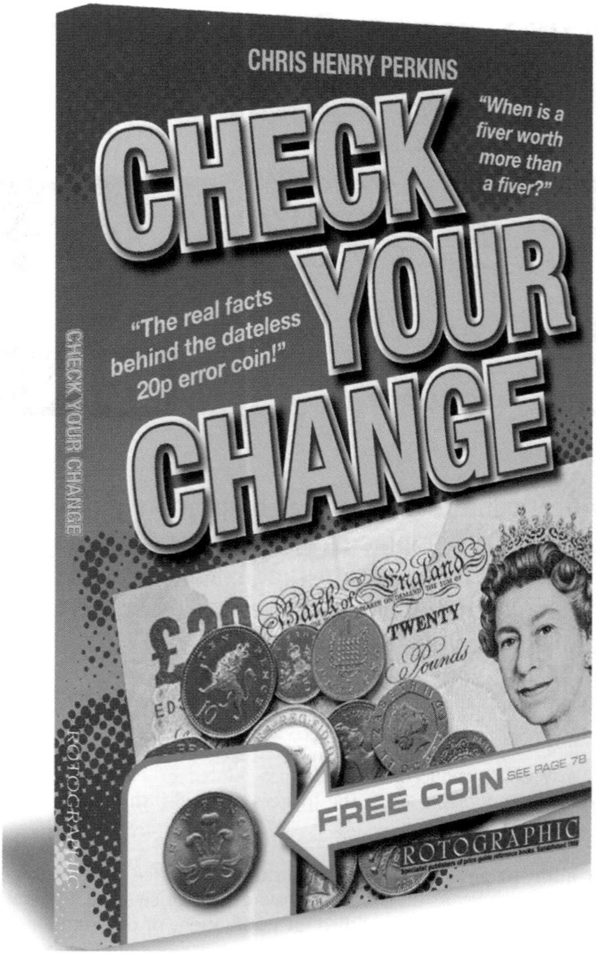
CHRIS HENRY PERKINS
CHECK YOUR CHANGE
"When is a fiver worth more than a fiver?"
"The real facts behind the dateless 20p error coin!"
CHECK YOUR CHANGE
ROTOGRAPHIC
FREE COIN
SEE PAGE 78
ROTOGRAPHIC

CONTENTS

Introduction and The Layout 4-5
How to use this book and important notes 5-11

Main Section: Circulation Coins and Mass produced Proof Coins
Fractional Farthings: 12
Farthings 15
Half Pennies 22
Pennies 31
Three Halfpence 44
Cartwheel Twopence 44
Threepences 46
Groats 51
Sixpences 52
Shillings 58
Eighteen Pences 66
Florins 66
Half Crowns 71
Three Shillings 78
Double Florins 79
Dollars 80
Crowns 81

Gold Section: Guinea & Sovereign based denominations 1797 - 1968
Introduction, Guineas, Half Guineas and Third Guineas 88
Introduction to Sovereign based denominations 90
Half Sovereigns 91
Sovereigns 98
Two Pound Coins 109
Five Pound Coins 110

Proof sets, 1826 to 1970 112
Maundy Section: Maundy sets and single Coins 113
Appendix I - A Glossary of Numismatic terms 117
Bibliography / Cover Coin / BM Copyright notice 118

INTRODUCTION

Welcome to "COLLECTORS' COINS GREAT BRITAIN 2012/13". If this is your first CCGB then thank you for purchasing and I hope it proves useful. CCGB is the most comprehensive British coin book covering British coins from the industrial revolution to the present day. If you already own a previous edition, then thanks again for your continued patronage.

As mentioned in the previous edition, post 1968 decimal coinage has been removed from this edition. This is mainly due to the huge numbers of new issues in recent years (there are well over 30 different Olympic coins alone, for example). "Check Your Change" (see p.2) is dedicated to decimals and goes into a lot more depth than would be practical here. From now on "Collectors' Coins GB" just covers the pre-decimal Pounds, Shillings and Pence, or L-S-D. These coins, despite being either a distant memory for most and even pre-dating a good proportion of the readership, remain the most collected and most collectable British coins. The coins that the masses didn't think about collecting, or couldn't afford to collect when they were new, will always be the most collectable. The reverse is also true: coins promoted as collectable and produced solely to be sold to 'collectors' are ironically usually the least collectable!

Also gone from this edition is the Proof section, which contained non mass produced, often experimental coins in odd or rarely used metals that were never intended for circulation. These coins are all rare and in some cases excessively rare! This rarity means that some don't often come up for sale and when they do, they can sell for much more than the last known sale. Price data is therefore difficult to maintain with any degree of accuracy. Other proof coins (mainly 20th century) that were made in larger numbers are still included in the main section.

It isn't all reductions though! With the extra space created from the removal of decimals and non mass-produced proofs I intend to gradually push back the coverage to encompass the whole of the reign of King George III. The first step has been made and in this edition the gold coverage has been extended to include the last of the Guinea based denominations. And all this in a book with a retail price of just Six Guineas (£6.30) for the 4th year in a row!

As ever, if you as a reader feel something else could be improved or even if there is something you don't like about this book, please feel free to visit the website, or call the number on the first page to have your say. I want to try to ensure that this book evolves and gets better every year, and I'm grateful for any kind of feedback.

Good luck with your collection or your price research.
Chris Perkins, August 2012

THE LAYOUT

Collectors' Coins Great Britain is laid out in three sections:

The Main section covers the period 1797-1970 and contains the main "Collectors' Coins", that is; all non-proof coins that were issued for circulation and the common mass produced proof coins. This section also covers some of the extremely rare coins of Edward VIII.

The Gold section covers Guineas, Half Guineas and Third Guineas 1797 to 1813 and Half Sovereigns, Sovereigns, Two Pound Coins and Five Pound coins struck from 1817 to 1968

The Maundy section contains Maundy sets and singles. These were never meant for circulation and are not proofs, so they too have been moved away from the general circulation section. As a bonus the proof sets from 1826 onwards are listed before the Maundy section.

HOW TO USE THIS PRICE GUIDE

The first (Main) and second (Gold) sections of this book are arranged in ascending order of face value, starting with the Fractional Farthing and working right up to the gold five pound coin. Each denomination is introduced and the average size and weight data is also specified. Each denomination is arranged in ascending date order, with each change in monarch clearly stated as well as major changes in the coin type.

All listings are split into columns, with a column each for the Date, Reference number (see next page), Mintage figure (also see next page) and the market values in 2-4 different grades. The Gothic florins have an extra column to show the date in Roman numerals and some of the Crowns have an extra column for the regnal edge year.

MINTAGE FIGURES

It is very important to realise that the mintage figures quoted in this book are very rarely accurate. Until the 1950's the Royal mint did not record the number of coins with a given date, but rather the number of coins struck in a particular year. So for example, the mintage of 1836 Farthings may be quoted as 1,290,240, but it is perfectly possible that a large proportion of those could have been dated 1835 (or even 1837). The mintage numbers do not record the number of coins that for certain types were re-melted either, so don't place any real relevance on the mintage numbers. They are just there to give a general feel for the numbers of coins produced.

INFORMATION ABOUT THE REFERENCE NUMBERS

Throughout this whole book, usually in the second column, you will notice there are reference numbers. The column in which these numbers appear will either be labelled 'PECK', 'FMAN' or 'ESC' and those abbreviations represent the books from which the reference number is taken. Many dealers will quote the numbers in these books when selling coins, as well as the date and condition. Although they are not normally referred to with newer coins. Every pre-decimal non gold coin in this catalogue has been labelled with its reference number from the following publications:

PECK = English Copper, Tin and Bronze Coins in the British Museum 1558-1958, by C Wilson Peck. All the Peck numbers in this book are preceded with a 'P' and all the Copper and Brass coins in this book are cross referenced with the Peck volume. Peck Numbers are sometimes referred to by other publications as 'BMC' (British Musuem Collection).

FMAN = The Bronze Coinage of Great Britain, by Michael J Freeman. This book, which is generally thought of as more up to date with Bronze coinage has been used to provide the reference numbers for all the Bronze coins in this book.

ESC = English Silver Coinage since 1649, by P Alan Rayner. This book has been used to provide reference numbers for all the Silver coins and Cupro-Nickel coins.

It is also important to bear in mind that not all of the coins listed in this book are referred to in the listed reference volumes, and where this is the case the initials **ND** (Not Distinguished) will appear in the reference number column. The initials **MV** are also used in places to indicate that Minor Varieties are in existence.

AN INTRODUCTION TO BRITISH COIN GRADING

The columns containing the market values in this book are headed by 2-4 Standard British coin grade names. Even novice coin collectors will probably realise that coins that are in better than average condition are always worth more than coins that have seen lots of circulation. Grading coins accurately takes a lot of experience in looking at the same types of coins, but, just as a rough idea this is what the grade columns stand for and mean:

Poor: These are not just smooth disks but actually identifiable coins. However, the list of shortcomings can be extensive, ranging from a few letters obliterated in the legend, to coins in which virtually the only detail visible is the date. Very few coins will still retain a value over and above the metal content, but they would need to be pretty rare.

Fair / Good: Heavily worn, but with readable legend and major points of design identifiable. It would be reasonable to say that the vast bulk of 20th century coins in this condition are worth no more than their metal value. Generally speaking, it has never been the practice to produce price data for coins in Fair condition.

F = Fine: Fine coins show considerable wear to all raised surfaces. Some detail should be visible on the designs and some of the main hair volume should be visible on the Monarch's head. Not individual strands, but maybe a parting or signs of head-dress. Many of the coins in your pocket even after just 30 years or less of normal use would probably be Fine or less.

VF = Very Fine: A coin with some wear to the highest areas of the design but which has seen limited circulation. More hair detail is evident and also detail on the other designs. Just as an average guide a coin that has been in normal circulation for approximately 5 years may qualify for VF status.

EF = Extremely Fine: A coin with little sign of being circulated. There may be only the slightest wear to the highest areas and minimal scratches and other marks. Often some of the mint lustre is visible on coins of this grade. As a rough idea a coin in your change would probably be an EF if it had been lucky and was minted just 1 year ago.

(Continued over the page)

AN INTRODUCTION TO BRITISH COIN GRADING (continued)

UNC = Uncirculated: Like the name suggests, the coin should be as it left the mint with no signs of circulation or wear. Not necessarily perfect though, because coins can pick up scratches and what are known as 'bag marks' during mass production and contact with other coins at the mint. The coin should have most of its lustre present and some dealers may expect 100% lustre on coins stated as Uncirculated. An Uncirculated coin would be given to you in your change from a freshly opened bag of new coins. So, as you can imagine, Uncirculated coins that are 30, 60 or even 200 years old, are often pretty rare, and very collectable, hence the higher prices for coins in this grade.

BU = Brilliant Uncirculated: BU is not really an official grade but is increasingly used to refer to an Uncirculated coin with full mint lustre. Such coins are also allowed to exhibit minor signs of mass production.

You may also see the grade FDC which is generally only used when talking about special proof strikings, and it means absolutely perfect in every way.

As well as the basic grades listed here, collectors will often encounter grades like 'GVF' for example. This indicates the coin is not exactly a 'VF' (Very Fine). In fact the 'G' stands for 'Good' so a GVF coin would be better that VF but not quite EF. 'N' stands for 'Near' and 'A' for 'About'. So, the range between VF and EF for example looks like this: VF, GVF, NEF, AEF, EF.

For further information, including images of all coin types in all the collectable grades, please see "The Standard Guide to Grading British Coins", shown on the opposing page.

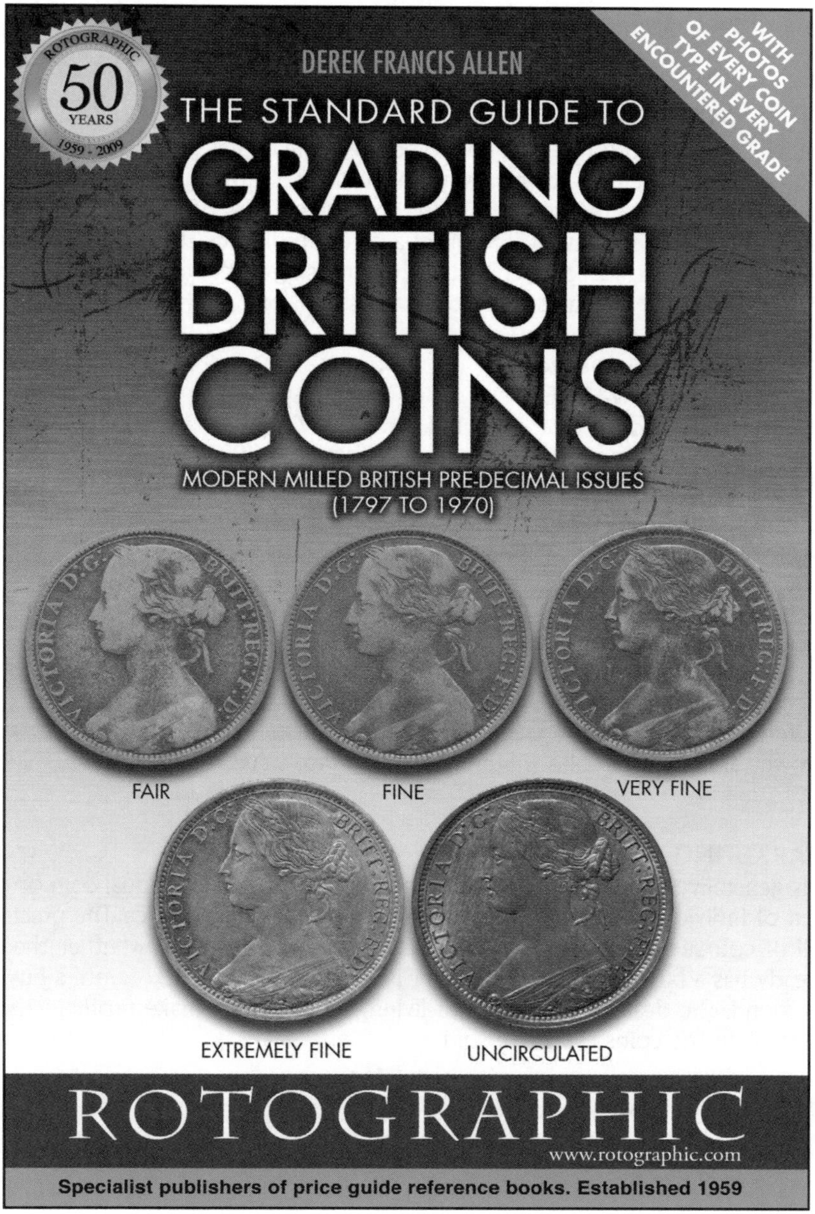

THE STANDARD GUIDE TO GRADING BRITISH COINS

Look out for The Standard Guide to Grading British Coins, also published by Rotographic. It's the where's wear of British pre decimal coinage. The only book to illustrate all the major coin types in all the major grades. The ISBN is: 978-0-948964-83-1. Price £12.99.

WHERE NO VALUE IS STATED

You will notice that for certain coin types only the higher grade columns are present. This is because these coins are not normally collected in lower grades. But that doesn't mean they are worthless in lower grades. Coins of all grades are there to be collected, and if you want to collect a date run of coins, then the grade doesn't really matter. There are some coins that have missing price data in one or more columns, this usually indicates that no data was available for that coin, in that grade.

SILVER BULLION VALUE

All British silver-coloured coins dated before 1947 contain silver, so even very worn coins are at least something. Silver coins dated pre 1920 are .925 (92.5% silver) and coins dated 1920-46 are .500 (50%) silver. The value of silver fluctuates, but generally dealers will gladly pay many times face value for all pre 1947 Silver coins. Decimal equivalent face values are as follows:

Each silver Threepence has a face value of 1/80th of a £ Sterling (1.25p).
Each Sixpence is 1/40th of a £ Sterling (2.5p).
Each Shilling is 1/20th of a £ Sterling (5p).
Each Florin is 1/10th of a £ Sterling (10p).
Halfcrowns are 1/8th of a £ Sterling (12.5p).
Crowns are a quarter of a £ Sterling, so 25p face value.

MARKETING

It is generally accepted that a dealer's buying price for an individual coin or collection of individual coins is about 50-75% of his/her selling price. The precise deal will of course depend on how sought after the items are, and whether the dealer already has a buyer in mind. The dealer is in effect out of pocket until a buyer can be found. The dealer has to make a living, and will only make profit in the long term when the coins can be re-sold.

CLEANING / POLISHING AND HANDLING OF COINS

DO NOT go anywhere near any coins with any chemicals / abrasives, or anything harder than a soft toothbrush. If your coins are dirty and are low grade, by all means use soap and water and perhaps a toothbrush to remove loose dirt. Make sure they are thoroughly dried, especially copper based coins. High grade and proof coins should ideally be handled by the edges or with gloves, because even the slightest finger print may knock significant value from the coin. If you have a valuable coin with a cosmetic problem, consult an expert first, or simply try to live with it.

VARIETIES / IF IN DOUBT

This book contains the most comprehensive listing of British coin varieties available for all denominations. However, it doesn't list every single variety. Many minute differences would need a whole page to explain, and don't always effect the value of the coins. For this reason some have been left out. If you have any queries about varieties or the contents of this book please consult www.rotographic.com and any important points that are raised will be covered in the next edition.

For further information on coin collecting or buying coins and collecting accessories why not ask at the place you purchased this book. Or if this book was purchased from a book retailer try an internet search on 'British Coins', 'British coins for sale' and similar phrases, or contact Rotographic via email or telephone for information about dealers in your area.

All fractional farthings were originally issued for colonial use. However, half farthings were made legal tender in the United Kingdom from 1842 - 1869. For that reason all fractional farthings have been listed.

Quarter Farthings

The tiny copper quarter farthing was struck solely for use in Ceylon (Sri Lanka). The maundy twopence die was used for the obverse. William Wyon was responsible for creating both the obverse and reverse dies.

VICTORIA Young head. Copper 13.5mm. Weight 1.175g

Date	Peck	Mintage	Fine	VF	EF	UNC/BU
1839	P1608	3,840,000	£12	£35	£75	£150/£200
1851	P1609	Inc below	£20	£50	£150	£220/
1852	P1610	2,215,000	£12	£35	£75	£150/£200
1853	P1612	Inc above	£15	£40	£89	£150/£200

Victoria 1839 Quarter Farthing

Third Farthings

Third Farthings were made for use in Malta. The farthing was already circulating at a face value of three Maltese grains so the third farthing was made to be exactly a third of the weight of a farthing, thus providing the Maltese with a coin of one grain face value. Obverse and reverse dies were by William Wyon.

GEORGE IV Copper 16mm. Weight 1.567g

Date	Peck	Mintage	Fine	VF	EF	UNC/BU
1827	P1453		£6	£20	£80	£200/

WILLIAM IV Copper 16mm. Weight 1.574g

Date	Peck	Mintage	Fine	VF	EF	UNC/BU
1835	P1477		£8	£20	£100	£200/

VICTORIA Young head. Copper 16mm. Weight 1.564g

Date	Peck	Mintage	Fine	VF	EF	UNC/BU
1844	P1606	1,301,040	£20	£40	£100	£250/
1844	ND	Large 'G'	£30	£60	£180	£350/
1844	P1607	RE instead of REG.	£40	£70	£300	£1000/
1844	ND. RE instead of REG but thinner flan, 0.88g. AUNC: £650 Cooke 2006					

George IV and William IV Third Farthings. The reverse types were the same.

Victoria 1844 Young head Third Farthing

Third Farthings (continued)

Third farthings from this point onwards were struck in bronze (95% copper, 4% tin and 1% zinc). Not being strictly British, they are not listed in the Freeman reference book, so Peck numbers are quoted instead. Victoria's bust and the reverses are the work of Leonard Charles Wyon, based on a model by W Theed. The portrait of Edward VII was modelled by G W de Saulles, and the portrait of George V by Sir Bertram Mackennal.

VICTORIA Bun head. Bronze 15.5mm. Weight 0.946g

Date	Peck	Mintage	Fine	VF	EF	UNC/BU
1866	P1926	576,000	£4	£10	£30	£80/
1866	ND	No stop after D.G				£150/
1868	P1928	144,000	£5	£10	£30	£90/
1876	P1932	162,000	£4	£15	£35	£100/
1878	P1933	288,000 Large date	£3	£10	£30	£90/
1878	ND	Small date	Scarcer			
1881	P1934	144,000	£3	£8	£30	£100/
1884	P1936	144,000	£3	£5	£30	£90/
1885	P1937	288,000	£3	£6	£30	£90/

EDWARD VII Bronze 15.5mm. Weight 0.957g

Date	Peck	Mintage	Fine	VF	EF	UNC/BU
1902	P2241	288,000	£3	£8	£20	£50/£60

GEORGE V Bronze 15.5mm. Weight 0.931g

Date	Peck	Mintage	Fine	VF	EF	UNC/BU
1913	P2358	288,000	£2	£5	£20	£40/

George V 1913 Third Farthing

Half Farthings

The half farthing, like the quarter farthing was originally struck for use in Ceylon (Sri Lanka). Willam Wyon was responsible for the obverse and reverse dies of the three monarchs under which half farthings were struck. The half farthing was made legal tender in the United Kingdom in 1842 and remained so until the demonetization of all the copper coinage in 1869.

GEORGE IV Laureate head. Copper 18mm. Weight 2.35g

Date	Peck	Mintage	Fine	VF	EF	UNC/BU
1828	P1446	7,680,000 Rev A	£20	£40	£130	£250/
1828	P1449	Rev B see below	£15	£40	£150	£300/
1828	ND	As above with large date. AVF: £200				
1830	P1450	8,776,320	£12	£40	£130	£250/
1830	ND	Smaller date	£50	£150	£300	
1830	P1451	Rev B see below	£40	£100	£250	

Rev A: The trident reaches above base of letters.
Rev B: The trident reaches base of letters.

George IV Half Farthing obverse. The reverse type was almost identical to the William IV reverse on the next page.

William IV Copper 18mm. Weight 2.313g

Date	Peck	Mintage	Fine	VF	EF	UNC/BU
1837	P1476	1,935,360	£40	£150	£400	£900/

George IV 1837 Half Farthing

Victoria Young head, Copper 18mm. Weight 2.365g

Date	Peck	Mintage	Fine	VF	EF	UNC/BU
1839	P1590	2,042,880	£5	£10	£40	£120/
1842	P1592		£4	£10	£40	£120/
1843	P1593	3,440,640	£3	£8	£35	£100/£125
1844	P1594	6,451,000	£3	£8	£30	£80/
1844	P1595	E of REGINA over N	£10	£30	£80	£200/£300
1847	P1596	3,010,560	£4	£7	£30	£100/
1847	ND	Last R of BRITANNIA over an A				£200/
1851	P1597		£4	£12	£50	£100/
1851	ND	1st 1 over 5	£10	£40	£100	£200/£300
1851	ND	5 struck over blundered number			£100	£200/
1852	P1598	989,184	£6	£20	£50	£100/
1853	P1599	955,224	£15	£40	£100	
1854	P1602	677,376	£10	£30	£90	
1856	P1603	913,920	£20	£40		
1856	ND	Large date and letters on Rev. NVF £200, NEF £400, both Cooke 2006				

Victoria 1844 Half Farthing

The farthings of 1799, 1806 and 1807 were all struck by Matthew Boulton at his mint in Soho, Birmingham. For the first time ever, a denomination was marked on a British coin, as the 1799 farthing had "1 Farthing" written in the exergue on the reverse. The Boulton Farthing dies were all engraved by Conrad Heinrich Küchler. The Laureate head of George IV was by Benedetto Pistrucci and the reverse by William Wyon.

GEORGE III Copper 23.5mm. Weight 6.298g

Date	Peck	Mintage	Fine	VF	EF	UNC/BU
1799	P1279	3 Berries in wreath	£4	£10	£45	£100/£150
1799	P1280	4 Berries in wreath	£10	£20	£70	£150/

George III 1799 Farthing

GEORGE III Copper 21mm. Weight 4.704g

Date	Peck	Mintage	Fine	VF	EF	UNC/BU
1806	P1396	Bust 1	£4	£12	£70	£170/
1806	P1397	Bust 2	£4	£10	£50	£150/
1806	P1398	Incuse dot on truncation		£50	£100	£300/
1807	P1399	Bust 1	£6	£20	£70	£150/£200

Bust 1: Curls of side whiskers are incuse, and the lower wreath leaves each have overlapping strands of hair. **Bust 2:** Curls are not incuse and the wreath leaves have no overlapping hair.

George III 1806 Farthing

GEORGE IV Laureate Head. Copper 22mm. Weight 4.749g

Date	Peck	Mintage	Fine	VF	EF	UNC/BU
1821	P1407	2,688,000	£2	£10	£60	£100/
1821	ND	G over O in GRATIA	£30		£200	(2009)
1822	P1409	5,924,352 Obv 1	£2	£10	£60	£100/
1822	P1411	Obv 2	£3	£10	£60	£100/
1823	P1412	2,365,440	£3	£12	£70	£100/
1823	P1413	Date has I for 1	£20	£100	£250	
1825	P1414	4,300,800 Obv 1	£2	£15	£70	£120/
1825	ND	5 over higher 5	£30		£200	
1825	ND	D of DEI over U	£30	£80	£250	
1825	P1415A	Obverse 2	£4	£15	£70	£120/
1826	P1416	6,666,240	£10	£15	£70	£120/
1826	ND	GRATIA R over E	£15	£70	£250	

George IV 1822 Farthing

GEORGE IV Bare Head. Copper 22mm. Weight 4.749g

Date	Peck	Mintage	Fine	VF	EF	UNC/BU
1826	P1439	Mintage included above	£2	£10	£60	£100/
1826	ND	Roman I for 1 (noted 2007)		£100	£300	
1827	P1442	2,365,440	£4	£10	£70	£140/
1828	P1443	2,365,440	£4	£12	£70	£100/£150
1829	P1444	1,505,280	£6	£20	£75	£180/
1830	P1445	2,365,440	£5	£15	£70	£140/£200

George IV 1827 Farthing

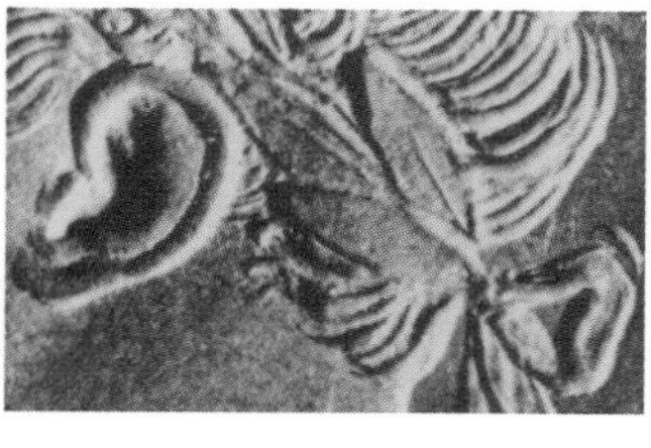

1822 and 1825 Obverse varieties.

Obverse 1: The leaf-midribs are single raised lines (left image).

Obverse 2: The 3 lowest leaves have incuse midribs (right image).

When the coin dies became worn, letters that were weak were re-cut using a punch. If the new letter or number was not in exactly the right place this led to the appearance of doubled and sometimes even trebled characters on the coin. This is commonplace during this period, however a major misalignment could add value to the coin.

William IV Copper 22mm. Weight 4.71g

Date	Peck	Mintage	Fine	VF	EF	UNC/BU
1831	P1466	2,68.8,000	£5	£12	£70	£150/
1834	P1470	1,935,360 Rev A	£4	£12	£75	£150/
1834	P1471	Reverse B	£10	£35	£100	£180/
1835	P1472	1,720,320 Rev A	£5	£25	£90	£170/
1835	P1473	Reverse B	£5	£20	£100	£180/
1836	P1474	1,290,240	£5	£20	£70	£120/£180
1837	P1475	3,010,560	£5	£20	£80	£180/
1837	ND	7 over 7 (misaligned)		£50	£150	£250/

Reverse A has an incuse line down the arms of the saltire (St Andrews cross).
Reverse B has a raised line down the arms of saltire.

William IV 1837 Farthing.

VICTORIA Young head. Copper 22mm. Weight 4.70g

Date	Peck	Mintage	Fine	VF	EF	UNC/BU
1838	P1553	591,360	£5	£12	£40	£140/
1838*	P1553	DEF. fullstop	£10	£30	£100	
1839	P1554	4,300,800	£4	£12	£50	£120/
1839	ND	'DEF' no stop	£10	£20	£70	£250/
1839	ND	Two-pronged trident			£200	£300/£400
1840	P1559	3,010,560	£3	£15	£50	£120/
1840	ND	Two-pronged trident				£300/
1840*	ND	'DEF.:' variety	£10	£30	£100	
1841	P1560	1,720,320	£4	£10	£50	£120/
1841	ND	Inverted 'V's for 'A's in GRATIA			£200 (2009)	
1841	ND	As above + dot in 1st 'A' in Britannia VF: £100 (2009)				
1841	ND	Varieties - REG. and REG for REG:				£200/
1842	P1562	1,290,240	£12	£50	£140	£300/
1842	ND	Large '42'	£30	£80	£200	
1843	P1563	4,085,760	£4	£12	£50	£100/£150
1843	P1564	I for 1 in date			£700	£1500/
1843	ND	3 over 2		£90	£250	
1844	P1565	430,080	£100	£200	£800	£2200/£2500
1845*	P1566	(A)	£10	£20	£60	£120/£200
1845*	ND	3,225,600 (B)	£12	£25	£70	£160/£250
1845	ND	Larger date	£90	£180		
1846	P1567	2,580,480	£12	£30	£100	
1847	P1568	3,879,720	£5	£20	£50	£130/
1848	P1569	1,290,246	£5	£20	£65	£130/

*1838 variety DEF. has just one dot where there should be a colon.
*1840 variety DEF.. has two horizontal dots where there should be a colon.
*1845 Type A has a normal straight '8'. Type B has an '8' which leans to the left.

Victoria 1857 (Young Head) Farthing

Date	Peck	Mintage	Fine	VF	EF	UNC/BU
1849	P1570	645,120	£35	£90	£350	£500/
1850	P1571	430,080 ?	£5	£20	£60	£120/
1850	ND	5 over inverted 5 or 3??		£40		£200/
1850	ND	5 over 4		£30	£150	£200/
1850	ND	Inverted 'V's for 'A's in Britannia			£150	
1851	P1572	1,935,360	£15	£30	£80	£200/
1851	P1573	D of 'DEI' struck over sideways 'D'	£200	£500	£1000/	
1852	P1574	822,528	£20	£40	£150	£250/
1853	P1575	1,028,628 W.W. raised	£4	£10	£50	£120/
1853	ND	3 over 2, raised W.W.		£40	£70	
1853	P1578	WW incuse	£8	£30	£120	£250/
1853	ND	Inverted V's for A's in BRITANNIA. VF:				£150
1854	P1580	6,504,960	£5	£20	£60	£120/
1855	P1581	3,440,640 WW incuse		£20	£60	£120/
1855	P1582	W.W. raised		£25	£80	£200/
1856	P1583	1,771,392	£7	£20	£80	£180/
1856*	P1584	E over R in Victoria	£30	£100	£200	
1857	P1585	1,075,200	£5	£15	£50	£120/
1858	P1586	1,720,320	£5	£15	£50	£120/
1858	ND	Small date	£50	£120		
1859	P1587	1,290,240	£20	£40	£100	£200/
1860	P1588	Obverse date, copper type				£10,000
1864	P1589	Obverse date. copper type				£15,000

*1856 E/R in VICTORIA. Also described as R over E. Either R was struck over an incorrect E, or E was wrongly selected to improve a poor R; (or ?)

Farthings from this point onwards were struck in bronze (95% copper, 4% tin and 1% zinc until 1923). Bronze was considered better than copper as it is more durable and wore at a slower rate. The coins were also more convenient sizes. The bun head Victorian farthing dies were engraved by Leonard Charles Wyon.

VICTORIA Bun head. Bronze 20mm. Weight 2.84g

BB = Border of Beads. TB = Toothed Border

Date	FMAN	Mintage	Fine	VF	EF	UNC/BU
1860		2,867,200 with various minor varieties, some rarer:				
1860	496	BB, 3 berries	£3	£10	£30	£100/
1860*	498	Beaded/toothed mule	£150	£400	£700	£1500/
1860	ND	Inverted reverse		(Cooke 2006)		£500/
1860	499	TB, 4 berries	£1	£6	£40	£120/
1860	501	TB, 5 berries	£1	£5	£40	£80/£130
1861	502	8,601,600. 4 berries	£2	£6	£40	£100/
1861	503	5 berries	£3	£6	£40	£95/£130
1861	ND	Date has small '8'	£3	£10	£50	£150/
1862	507	14,336,000	£1	£5	£40	£100/
1862	ND	Large fat '8'			£700	
1862	ND	Small '8' over large '8'		£100		
1863	509	1,433,600	£25	£50	£200	£400/
1863	ND	Dot below lighthouse (London Coins 2007)	(Cooke 2006)	GVF: £90		£400/£500

Victoria 1860 toothed rim Farthing

Date	FMAN	Mintage	Fine	VF	EF	UNC/BU
1864	511A	2,508,800 serif 4*	£5	£12	£50	£140/
1864	511	plain 4*	£2	£6	£40	£120/
1865	512	4,659,200	£2	£5	£35	£90/
1865	513	5 over 2	£3	£10	£50	£120/
1865	ND	5 over 3	£4	£10	£50	£120/
1865	ND	Date has small '8'	£2	£8	£35	£100/
1866	514	3,584,000	£1	£4	£35	£100/
1866	ND	RFG for REG (broken die)		£20	£60	£150/
1866	ND	widely spaced 6's	£1	£10	£50	£120/
1867	516	5,017,600	£2	£5	£40	£120/
1868	519	4,851,208	£2	£6	£40	£130/
1869	522	3,225,600	£5	£20	£60	£150/
1872	523	2,150,400	£4	£10	£55	£100/
1873	524	3,225,620	£2	£6	£40	£100/
1873	ND	Low set 3 in date	£4	£20	£80	£200/
1875	528	Large date (5 berries)	£6	£30	£70	
1875	529	Small date (4 berries)	£10	£40	£150	£340/
1875H	530	Small date (5 berries) with Full rose brooch visible on bodice. Extremely Rare, and not to be confused with the very common slightly aged obverse type below. VF: £425				
1874H	525	3,584,000	£2	£10	£50	£120/
1874H	527	G's struck over sideways G's		£500		
1875	531	712,760 (for more '1875' details contact Rotographic)				
		Small date, 4 berries	£10	£25	£100	£200/£350
1875H	532	6,092,800, 4 berries	£1	£3	£30	£90/
1875H	ND	5 over 2 noted 1999			£50	
1875H	ND*	RF.G for REG	£1	£3	£30	£90/
* A fairly common die break.						
1876H	534	1,175,200	£5	£10	£40	£100/
1876H	534A	Large 6 in date	£10	£30	£90	£150/
1876H	ND*	RF.G for REG die break	£5	£25	£75	£180/£240
1877		Proof Only				
1878	536	4,008,540	£1	£3	£30	£100/
1879	538	3,977,180	£4	£10	£30	£80/£120
1879	540	Date has large '9'	£6	£20	£50	£100/
1880	541	1,842,710 (4 berries)	£1	£5	£40	£100/
1880	543	(3 berries)	£10	£80	£150	£300/£400
1881	544	4 berries (incl below)		£50		£175/
1881	545-6	3,494,670. 3 berries	£2	£7	£30	£100/
1881H	548	1,792,000	£1	£5	£30	£100/
1881H	ND	H further to left			£250	
1882H	549	1,790,000	£2	£5	£30	£100/
1883	551	1,128,680	£3	£8	£40	£100/
1884	553	5,782,000	£1	£3	£20	£70/
1885	555	5,442,308	£1	£3	£20	£70/
1886	557	7,767,790	£1	£4	£20	£70/
1887	559	1,340,800	£1	£4	£30	£100/
1888	560	1,887,250	£1	£4	£30	£80/
1890	562	2,133,070	£1	£4	£30	£80/
1891	564	4,959,690	£1	£4	£25	£75/

*1864 - Plain and serif '4' in date: See the penny section for more details.

'H' centred below date = Heaton Mint (Coin was not made at the Royal Mint)

All Royal Mint coins 1875 to 1878 have an 'R' with a forked tail; the Heaton Mint issues do not. So an 1875 with forked 'R' might well be an 1875H with 'H' removed to Increase value!

During the 35 year run of bun-head farthings, minor changes were occasionally made to age the queens portrait

Minor die varieties of 1881H Farthings occur, but a whole extra book would be needed to point out the intricate but very minor differences!

Date	FMAN	Mintage	Fine	VF	EF	UNC/BU
1892	566	887,240	£5	£10	£50	£150/
1893	568	3,904,320	£1	£4	£25	£75/£90
1893	ND	Narrower date	£2	£8	£40	£150/
1894	569	2,396,770	£1	£7	£30	£75/£100
1895	570	2,852,853	£10	£25	£90	£250/

The veiled head Victoria portrait was engraved by George William de Saulles, from a Model by Thomas Brock. The reverse was also the work of de Saulles. Most of the 1897 farthings, and all farthings up to 1917 were chemically darkened, to avoid them being confused for half sovereigns, which were a very similar size.

VICTORIA Old or widow head. Bronze 20mm. Weight 2.857g

Date	FMAN	Mintage	Fine	VF	EF	UNC/BU
1895	571	Inc with bun head	£1	£3	£10	£30/£40
1896	572	3,668,610		£2	£8	£35/
1897	ND	Bright finish			£15	£40/£60
1897		4,579,800 Blackened.				
1897*	574	Horizon as 1896	£1	£3	£13	£30/£40
1897**	575	Higher horizon	£1	£3	£13	£30/£50
1898	576	4,010,080		£2	£10	£30/£40
1899	577	3,864,616		£1	£10	£40/£55
1900	578	5,969,317		£2	£10	£25/£40
1901	579	8,016,459		£1	£8	£20/£25
1901	ND	Bright finish error				/£100

* = The '7' points to a border tooth. ** = The '7' points between two teeth

Victoria 1897 Farthing

George William de Saulles was also responsible for the engraving of the dies for the Edward VII farthings. The reverse remained very similar to the last Victorian farthings.

EDWARD VII Bronze 20mm. Weight 2.834g

Date	FMAN	Mintage	Fine	VF	EF	UNC/BU
1902	580	5,125,120. A		£2	£10	£25/£30
1902	ND	Incl above. B		£2	£10	£30/£40
1903	581	5,331,200	£1	£4	£12	£40/£50
1904	582	3,628,800	£1	£4	£15	£25/£30
1904	ND	Bright finish error				£80/
1905	583	4,076,800		£4	£20	£45/
1906	584	5,340,160		£3	£20	£40/£50
1907	585	4,399,360		£2	£15	£30/
1908	586	4,264,960		£4	£15	£35/£45
1909	587	8,852,480		£2	£15	£35/£45
1910	588	2,598,400	£1	£4	£20	£35/£50

Type A: Weak strike - patchy breastplate on Britannia.
Type B: Well struck - clear design work.

All Edward VII Farthings were Chemically darkened and had the Britannia reverse in the same style as old head Victorian farthings. The obverse used the standard portrait of the King.

Farthings of George V, VI and Elizabeth II

The portrait of George V was the work of Sir Bertram Mackennal. The reverse was a slightly altered version of the Edward VII reverse type. The farthings of George VI saw a departure from the traditional designs of former years, and a Wren by H Wilson Parker was chosen to be used as a new reverse type. The George VI portrait was the work of T H Paget. The bust of Elizabeth II was the work of Mary Gillick and the Wren reverse was also used on the Elizabeth II farthings until the last 1956 dated coins.

GEORGE V Bronze 20mm. Weight 2.821g

Date	FMAN	Mintage	VF	EF	UNC/BU
1911	589	5,196,800 *1a	£2	£8	£20/£30
1911	ND	*1b (see right)	£3	£8	£20/£30
1912	590	7,669,760		£4	£12/£18
1913	591	4,134,320		£3	£12/£18
1914	592	6,126,988 BRITT Obv.1		£8	£24/£30
1914	593	BRIT_T (gap)		£8	£20/£30
1915	593A	BRITT (no gap)			£250/£350
1915	594	7,129,254 BRIT_T	£1	£10	£35/
1916	595	10,993,325		£3	£15/
1917	596	21,434,844		£2	£15/
1918	597	19,362,818 Bright			£20/£30
1918	ND	Scarcer, darkened finish		£10	£30/
1919	598	15,089,425		£2	£10/£15
1920	599	11,480,536		£2	£10/£15
1921	600	9,469,097		£2	£10/£15
1922	601	9,956,983		£2	£10/£15
1923	602	8,034,457		£3	£10/£20
1924	603	8,733,414		£2	£10/£14
1925	604	12,634,697		£10	£20/
1926	605	9,792,397		£1	£12/
1927	607	7,868,355		£1	£12/
1928	609	11,625,600		£1	£8/£12
1929	611	8,419, 200		£1	£10/£15
1930	613	4,195,200		£1	£10/£12
1931	615	6,595,200		£1	£8/£12
1932	617	9,292,800		£1	£10/£12
1933	619	4,560,000		£1	£8/£12
1934	621	3,052,800		£3	£8/£15
1935	623	2,227,200	£2	£5	£20/£25
1936	625	9,734,400		£1	£10/£14

*1911 - Obv 1a: Above B.M. the neck is hollow. Obv 1b: Above B.M. the neck is flat.

1914 & 1915:
Varieties with different spacing between the T's in BRITT occur. BRITT represents close spacing, and BRIT_T represents far spacing.

George V 1921 Farthing

EDWARD VIII

Date	FMAN	Mintage	UNC/BU
1937	627	Extremely rare £20,000+ (not issued for general circulation)	

GEORGE VI Bronze 20mm. Weight 2.838g

Date	FMAN	Mintage	UNC/BU
1937	628	8,131,200	£5/£7
1937	629	26,402 Proofs	£5/£8
1938	630	7,449,600	£6/£10
1939	632	31,440,000	£5/£7
1940	634	18,360,000	£5/£7
1941	636	27,312,000	£5/£7
1942	638	28,857,600	£5/£7
1943	640	33,345,600	£5/£7
1944	642	25,137,600	£5/£7
1945	644	23,736,000	£5/£7

George VI 1943 Farthing

Elizabeth II 1954 Farthing. The wren type reverse was also used for the farthings of Elizabeth II

GEORGE VI Bronze 20mm. Weight 2.838g

Date	FMAN	Mintage	UNC/BU
1946	646	23,364,800	£5/£7
1947	648	14,745,600	£5/£7
1948	650	16,622,400	£5/£7
1949	652	8,424,000	£5/£7
1950	654	10,324,800	£5/£7
1950	655	17,513 Proofs	£10/£14
1951	656	14,016,000	£6/£10
1951	657	20,000 Proofs	£10/£14
1952	658	5,251,200	£7/£10

ELIZABETH II Bronze 20mm. Weight 2.852g

Date	FMAN	Mintage	EF	UNC/BU
1953		6,131,037 :		
	660	Obverse 1 Reverse A, From set		£5/£7
	661	Obverse 1 Reverse B	£2	£15/£25
	662	Obverse 2 Reverse A	£3	£20/£30
	663	Obverse 2 Reverse B		£3/£7
	664	40,000 Proofs		£5/£7
	662A	Proof Obverse 2 + Reverse A		£70/£100
1954	665	6,566,400		£3/£5
1955	667	5,779,200		£3/£5
1956	669	1,996,800	£2	£10/£15

Obverse 1: Is poorly defined. The cross points TO a border bead.
Obverse 2: Is sharper. The cross points BETWEEN two border beads.
Reverse A: (uses the dies of George VI) - The 'F' points BETWEEN two beads.
Reverse B: Is similar, but the 'F' points TO a border bead.

1953 Obverse/Reverse Rarity Scale 1 + A is scarce. 2 + A is rare. 1 + B is rare. 2 + B is very common.

Halfpennies

The 1799 halfpenny was the first official halfpenny issue since 1775. Following on from the successful introduction of the Cartwheel Twopence and Penny in 1797, Matthew Boulton also produced the 1799 and 1806/07 Halfpennies. The dies were prepared by Conrad Heinrich Küchler.

GEORGE III Soho Mint, Copper 31mm. Weight 12.659g

Date	Peck	Mintage	Fine	VF	EF	UNC/BU
1799	P1248	5 incuse ship gunports	£3	£8	£60	£200/
1799	P1249	6 raised ship gunports	£3	£8	£70	£200/
1799	P1250	9 raised ship gunports	£3	£8	£80	£200/
1799	P1251	Plain ship hull	£3	£9	£70	£200/
1799	P1252	Raised line on ship, no guns	£3	£9	£60	£200/

2nd type, Soho Mint, Copper 29mm. Weight 9.428g

Date	Peck	Mintage	Fine	VF	EF	UNC/BU
1806	P1376	Olive branch no berries	£5	£10	£50	£120/
1806	ND	Ball under trident prongs, which is normally only seen on the proof varieties. Reported on predecimal.com 2006.				
1806	P1377	3 berries 'SOHO' *	£5	£10	£60	£150/
1807	P1378	3 berries 'SOHO' *	£5	£10	£55	£150/

* The word SOHO is underlined on the reverse of the coin.

1799 Soho Halfpenny

1806 Soho Halfpenny

The copper halfpennies of George IV, William IV and Victoria are all the work of William Wyon (although the portrait of William IV was based on a model by Sir Francis Chantry). The reverse type remained the same until REG replaced REX for the issues struck under Queen Victoria.

GEORGE IV Laureate head, Copper 28mm. Weight 9.337g

Date	Peck	Mintage	Fine	VF	EF	UNC/BU
1825	P1431	215,040	£12	£30	£150	£300/
1826	P1433	9,031,630, Rev A	£6	£25	£100	£240/
1826	P1436	Rev B	£8	£30	£120	£250/
1827	P1438	5,376,000	£7	£25	£100	£250/

1826: Rev A: The saltire of shield has two incuse lines. Rev B: The saltire of shield has one raised line.

The saltire/St. Andrew's cross, is often divided by lines. More info about the St.Andrews cross and similar varieties can be found in the George IV penny section.

WILLIAM IV Bare head, Copper 28mm. Weight 9.389g

Date	Peck	Mintage	Fine	VF	EF	UNC/BU
1831	P1461	806,400	£12	£25	£100	£250/
1834	P1464	537,600	£12	£25	£100	£250/
1837	P1465	349,400	£12	£25	£100	£250/
1837	ND	Small date over large			£150	

VICTORIA Young head with date below, Copper 28mm. Weight 9.457g

Date	Peck	Mintage	Fine	VF	EF	UNC/BU
1838	P1522	456,960	£6	£15	£70	£180/
1841	P1524	1,075,200	£5	£12	£60	£150/
1841	ND	Broken die: DEI reads DF.I			£100	
1841	ND	Alignment Up/down (Ap I)	£20	£50	£200	
1843	P1527	967,680	£20	£50	£200	
1844	P1528	1,075,200	£10	£20	£70	£160/
1845	P1529	1,075,200	£80	£250		
1846	P1530	860,160	£8	£20	£80	£140/
1847	P1531	752,640	£5	£25	£80	£120/
1848	P1533	322,560	£10	£50	£150	£300/

George IV 1826 Halfpenny

William IV 1837 Halfpenny

On the next page some of the 1850s halfpennies have either no dots near the shield (left image) or 7 incuse dots on and around the shield (right image)

VICTORIA Young head with date below, Copper 28mm. Weight 9.457g

Date	Peck	Mintage	Fine	VF	EF	UNC/BU
1848	P1532	8 struck over 7	£6	£20	£100	£240/
1848	ND	8 struck over 3	£5	£20	£100	
1851	P1534	215,040 no dots on or above shield		£20	£70	£200/
1851	P1535	Shield, 7 incuse dots	£6	£15	£50	£120/
1852	P1536	637,056 (no dots)	£5	£20	£70	£200/
1852	P1537	Shield, 7 incuse dots	£6	£15	£60	£130/
1853	P1539	1,559,040	£3	£9	£40	£120/
1853	P1538	3 over 2	£8	£30	£120	
1854	P1542	12,354,048 ?	£4	£10	£50	£100/
1855	P1543	1,455,837	£4	£10	£50	£100/
1856	P1544	1,942,080	£4	£10	£60	£180/
1856	ND	6 over larger 6 (values perhaps a little more than above)				
1857	P1545	Shield, 7 incuse dots	£5	£15	£60	£180/
1857	P1546	1,182,720 (no dots)	£7	£20	£70	£200/
1858	P1549	2,472,960	£5	£10	£70	£150/
1858	ND	Smaller date	£5	£15	£70	£150/
1858	P1547	Last 8 over 6	£5	£15	£80	£150/
1858	P1548	Last 8 over 7	£5	£12	£80	£150/
1859	P1551	1,290,340	£8	£15	£80	£150/
1859	P1550	9 struck over 8	£6	£20	£100	£250/
1860*	P1552	Extremely rare	£300	£1000	£4000	£5000/

*Copper type - Date is below head, not below Britannia.

Victoria 1853 Halfpenny

In 1860 the first bronze halfpennies were produced in line with the bronze alloy used for the farthings and pennies. The dies were the work of Leonard Charles Wyon. Massive demands were made on the Royal Mint and as a result of this some coins were struck by private mints in Birmingham to ease the workload.

VICTORIA 'Bun' head, date on reverse, Bronze 26mm. Weight 5.693g

Beaded Borders:

Date	FMAN	Mintage	Fine	VF	EF	UNC/BU
1860	258	Obv 1	£3	£10	£50	£150/
(Freeman 258 has 2 slightly different reverses, distinguishable by the differences in the length of Britannia's hair)						
1860	260A	Obv 1*		£50		
1860	260C	Mule toothed/beaded borders (Coincraft 1995) £1000				
Toothed borders:						
1860	261	Obv 2, Rev B	£2	£8	£60	£150/£200
1860	264	Obv 2, Rev C	£2	£8	£60	£150/£200
1860	265	Obv 3, Rev B	£2	£8	£70	£180/£220
1860	266	Obv 4, Rev B	£4	£12	£70	£180/£220
1860	267	Obv 4, Rev C			£200	£300/
1860	ND	F of HALF over P	£250			
1861 - 12 minor varieties occur, most dealers do not distinguish.						
1861	269-82	54,118,400	£3	£8	£70	£200/
1861	274A/82A	6 over 8	£1000 (Fine)			
1861	279	Last 1 over lower 1 reported on predecimal.com forum.				
1861	ND	R over B in BRITT. See illustration opposite.				

Obv 1 has 6 berries in the wreath arranged in pairs. Obv 1* is as Obv 1 with minor changes - the knot in the hair tie has been removed. Obv 2 has 7 berries. Obv 3 has 5 berries. Obv 4 has 4 berries.

Reverse types: B - lighthouse tapering, pointed. C - lighthouse cylindrical with rounded top. Some 1860 Bun head Halfpennies bear F's with little or no lower serif to the lower horizontal bar.

1861 Halfpenny detail showing the R over B in BRITT. First made public on the Predecimal.com forum by Gary Brett.

LONDON
COINS
DEALERS AND AUCTIONEERS
FREE VALUATIONS AND APPRAISALS
* English Milled Coins
* British Hammered Coins
* World Coins
* Roman and Ancient Coins
* Proof Sets
* Royal Mint Issues
* Paper Money
* Medals
* Gold Coins, Sovereigns, Guineas and Krugerrands
* Tokens
* Bonds and Shares
Free Catalogues
'How To Sell Your Coins' Information Pack
See our website for our stock of choice English coins
www.londoncoins.co.uk
Four auctions every year
4-6 Upper Street South
New Ash Green, Longfield, Kent, DA3 8JJ
Tel: 01474 871464

VICTORIA 'Bun' head

Date	FMAN	Mintage	Fine	VF	EF	UNC/BU
1862	289	61,107,200	£2	£6	£50	£150/
1862	288	B to left of Lighthouse. VG: £260 (2006)				
1862	288A	C to left of Lighthouse				£2000+?
1862	290A	Unbarred A left of lighthouse. AUNC: £1600 (2008)				
1863	292	15,948,800	£2	£8	£65	£240/
1863	294	With smaller straighter '3'.		£30		£260/
1864	295	537,600	£4	£10	£70	£250/
1865	296	8,064,000		£20	£90	£250/
1865	297	5 over 3	£35	£75	£250	£600/
1866	298	2,508,800	£5	£14	£70	£250/
1867	300	2,508,806	£5	£15	£80	£250/
1868	303	3,046,400	£5	£15	£75	£250/
1869	306	3,225,600	£20	£100	£300	£800/
1870	307	4,350,739	£5	£16	£70	£180/
1871	308	1,075,280 ?	£20	£100	£300	£700/
1872	309A	4,659,410	£5	£10	£60	£180/
1873	310	3,404,880	£5	£12	£60	£175/
1873	311	Upper and lower arms of St. Andrews cross slightly out of line with each other.			£120	
1874	312-317	1,347,665 16 Wreath leaves	£10	£32	£100	£300/
1874H	318	5,017,600	£5	£15	£60	£170/
1875	321-322A	5,430,815. MV	£5	£16	£60	£170/
1875H	323	1,254,400	£5	£15	£60	£170/
1876H	325-329	6,809,600. MV	£5	£15	£60	£170/
1877	330-334	5,209,505. MV	£5	£14	£50	£160/£200
1878	334/5/7	1,425,535. MV	£10	£30	£150	£300/£400
1879	338/9	3,582,545. MV	£6	£10	£60	£140/
1880	340/41A	2,423,465. MV	£2	£5	£50	£160/
1881	342/43A	2,007,515. MV	£4	£8	£50	£160/
1881H	344	1,792,000	£4	£8	£50	£160/
1882H	347	4,480,000	£4	£8	£50	£160/
1883	349	3,000,725. Brooch*	£4	£8	£50	£160/
1883	348/348A/351	Rose*. MV		£50	£100	£200/

Victorian Bun head 1888 Halfpenny

MV = Minor varieties exist. Varieties not generally distinguished by most dealers and specialist reading is required for further identification details.

*1863 - Varieties in the style of the '3' in the date. One has a larger upper section and both are thought to exist in approximately equal numbers.
*1883 - At the Queen's neckline is either a small brooch or a small rose. The brooch consists of a large oblong shape with 6 ovals surrounding it.

VICTORIA 'Bun' head, date on reverse, Bronze 26mm. Weight 5.693g

Date	FMAN	Mintage	Fine	VF	EF	UNC/BU
1884	352	6,939,580	£4	£8	£50	£150/
1885	354	8,600,574	£4	£8	£50	£150/
1886	356	8,586,155	£4	£8	£50	£150/
1887	358	10,701,305	£2	£6	£40	£140/
1888	359	6,814,070	£2	£6	£40	£140/
1889	360	7,748,234	£1	£5	£50	£140/
1889	361	9 over 8	£10	£50	£150	£300/
1890	362	11,254,235	£1	£6	£40	£80/
1891	364	13,192,260	£1	£5	£40	£80/
1892	366	2,478,335	£2	£6	£50	£150/
1893	368	7,229,344	£1	£5	£50	£150/
1894	369	1,767,635	£3	£10	£40	£150/

VICTORIA Old or widow head. Bronze 26mm. Weight 5.644g

The obverse for this issue was engraved by George William de Saulles from a model by Thomas Brock, whose initials appear under the shoulder. The reverse is a modified version of the Leonard Charles Wyon design, with the lighthouse and ship removed.

Date	FMAN	Mintage	Fine	VF	EF	UNC/BU
1895	370	3,032,154	£1	£3	£10	£40/£55
1896	371/2	9,142,500. MV	£1	£2	£10	£30/£40
1897	374	8,690,315	£1	£2	£10	£30/£45
1897	373	Higher tide *	£2	£4	£15	£35/£50
1898	375	8,595,180	£1	£3	£15	£30/£50
1899	376	12,108,001	£1	£3	£10	£30/£50
1900	377	13,805,190	£1	£2	£10	£25/£40
1901	378	11,127,360	£1	£2	£8	£20/£30

* The 1897 higher tide variety has a tide level with the folds in Britannia's robe. The normal tide type has a tide level with the bottom of the robe. The veiled head Victorian Halfpenny was very similar in style to the penny.

EDWARD VII Britannia Reverse, Bronze 26mm. Weight 5.67g

The obverse of this issue was also engraved by George William de Saulles. Initially the same reverse was used as previously.

Date	FMAN	Mintage	Fine	VF	EF	UNC/BU
1902	380	Low tide,	£1	£50	£100	£250/
1902	381	13,672,960 High tide		£2	£8	£25/£35
1903	382	11,450,880		£2	£15	£40/£50
1904	383	8,131,200	£3	£6	£20	£60/£80
1905	384	10,124,800		£5	£20	£45/£65
1906	385	11,101,440		£3	£15	£40/£60
1907	386	16,849,280		£3	£12	£30/£50
1908	387	16,620,800		£3	£12	£30/£40
1909	388	8,279,040		£4	£15	£40/£60
1910	389	10,769,920		£2	£10	£35/£50

1905 Halfpenny

The Low Tide variety referred to above and in the Edward VII penny section may be determined thus: if the horizon meets Britannia at the point below the knee, where right and left legs cross; NORMAL tide is indicated. If, however, the horizon meets Britannia at a much lower point - nearer the hem of her drape - then a LOW TIDE variety has been detected. Comparison with a normal tide other date Edward VII coin makes it much easier to tell.

The BM initials on the truncation of George V stand for Bertram Mackennal, the designer of the George V bust. The first reverse type was identical to that used for Edward VII. Unlike the pennies, there are no 'H' or 'KN' halfpennies, instead, many of the blanks produced for George V halfpennies were made by private firms in Birmingham. There were problems with 'ghosting' (the faint outline of one side appearing on the other side) for this issue throughout most of the reign. Despite the bronze alloy being changed in 1923 (to 95.5% copper, 3% tin and 1.5% zinc) and the head being modified in 1925, this problem was not completely solved until the issue of the smaller head type in 1928.

GEORGE V Britannia Reverse, Bronze 26mm. Weight 5.658g

Date	FMAN	Mintage	VF	EF	UNC/BU
1911		12,570,880			
	390	*Obverse 1a	£2	£7	£25/£35
1911	ND	*Obverse 1b	£3	£8	£25/£35
1912	391	21,185,920	£2	£8	£28/£35
1913	392	17,476,480	£2	£8	£30/£40
1914	393	20,289,111	£2	£8	£30/£40
1915	394	21,563,040	£5	£12	£35/
1916	395	39,386,143	£1	£8	£30/
1917	396	38,245,436	£1	£8	£30/£40
1918	397	22,321,072	£1	£8	£30/£40
1919	398	28,104,001	£1	£8	£30/£45
1920	399	35,146,793	£1	£8	£30/£40
1921	400	28,027,293	£1	£8	£28/£35
1922	401	10,734,964	£2	£10	£40/£50
1923	402	12,266,282	£1	£8	£28/£40
1924	403	13,971,038	£1	£10	£30/£40
1925	404	12,216,123 Head as For 1924	£1	£6	£30/£40
1925	405	Modified effigy as for 1926, see appendix 1			
			£3	£10	£35/£50
1926	406	6,712,306	£2	£6	£30/£40
1927	408	15,589,622	£1	£6	£25/£35
Smaller Head:					
1928	410	20,935,200	£1	£5	£24/£35
1929	412	25,680,000	£1	£14	£50/£65
1930	414	12,532,800	£1	£6	£20/£35
1931	416	16,137,600	£1	£6	£20/£30
1932	418	14,448,000	£1	£5	£20/£30
1933	420	10,560,000	£1	£5	£20/£30
1934	422	7,704,000	£1	£6	£24/£30
1935	424	12,180,000	£1	£3	£20/£30
1936	426	23,008,800	£1	£3	£12/£20

1911* Obverse 1a has a hollow neck.
Obverse 1b has a flat neck.

1911 & 1912: Some dies were punched with date close to line of exergue.
Small gap = Rev A.
Clear gap = Rev B.

Combinations:: 1a+A 1a+B 1b+A 1b+B.

Most dealers do not differentiate.

George V Halfpenny 1913

George V Halfpenny 1931
(Smaller head and modified Britannia)

EDWARD VIII Reverse Golden Hind ship, Bronze 26mm

1937	Excessively rare, impossible to value.

As with the farthings of George VI, the decision was taken to break from tradition and change the reverse on the halfpennies too. Both the obverse and reverse were designed by Thomas Humphey Paget, whose initials appear to the right of the Golden Hind on the reverse.

GEORGE VI Reverse Golden Hind ship, Bronze 26mm. Weight 5.7g

Date	FMAN	Mintage	EF	UNC/BU
1937	429	24,504,000	£1	£5/£7
1937	430	26,402 proofs		£8/£10
1938	431	40,320,000	£1	£8/£10
1939	433	28,924,800	£2	£15/£18
1940*	437/8	32,162,400	£2	£15/£18
1940	435	Thin rim, short teeth		£10/£20
1941	439	45,120,000	£1	£8/£10
1942	441	17,908,800	£1	£7/£8
1943	443	76,200,000	£1	£6/£7
1944	445	81,840,000	£1	£7/£8
1945	447	57,000,000	£1	£7/£8
1946	449	22,725,600	£2	£10/£15
1947	451	21,266,400	£1	£7/£8
1948	453	26,947,200	£1	£7/£8

*1940: 3 varieties - Type 1: 'L' points between beads and the 'P' points to a bead. Type 2: 'L' and 'P' point between beads. Type 3: The 'L' points to a bead (see 'Pointings', appendix I)

These varieties are rarely distinguished, and the prices are usually the same for each.

From 1949 the title IND:IMP (Emperor of India) was removed due to the India of the British Raj becoming two independent states (India and Pakistan).

Date	FMAN	Mintage	EF	UNC/BU
1949	455	24,744,000	£1	£10/£15
1950	457	24,153,600	£2	£10/£12
1950	458	17,513 Proofs FDC		£12
1951	459	14,868,000	£3	£15/£25
1951	460	Proofs 20,000 FDC		£10
1952	461	33,278,400	£2	£20/£25

George VI Halfpenny 1945

Elizabeth II 1959 Halfpenny

The Golden Hind vessel was continued as the reverse type on the Halfpennies of Elizabeth II. Mary Gillick designed the obverse portrait, and her initials appear on the centre of the truncation of the shoulder. The first coins issued in 1953 had a very low relief portrait and showed very little detail, particularly in the hair area. The obverse die was re-cut during 1953, leading to the two slight varieties for that year. In 1954 the BRITT:OMN (of all the Britons) title was removed due to the changing state of the fading British Empire.

ELIZABETH II Reverse Golden Hind ship, Bronze 26mm. Weight 5.658g

Date	FMAN	Mintage	EF	UNC/BU
1953		8,910,000:		
1953	463	Obverse 1		£3/£5
1953	464	Obverse 2		£1/£2
1953	465/A	40,000 Proofs. MV		£3/£6
1954	466/8	19,375,200.MV	£6	£25/£35
1955	469	18,465,600		£4/£5
1956	471-5	21,799,200.MV		£5/£6
1957	477	39,672,000		£2/£3
1957*	476	Calmer sea rev	£6	£25/£40
1958	479/80	66,331,200. MV		£2/£3
	481	Thicker rim, shorter teeth		£150/
1959	483	79,176,000		£2/£3
1960	485	41,340,000		£4/£5
1962	487	41,779,200		£2/£3
1963	489	42,720,000		£2/£3
1964	491	78,583,200		£1/£2
1965	492	98,083,200		£1/£2
1965	ND	Error N.Zealand Rev		£450
1966	493	95,289,600		50p/£1
1967*	494	146,490,400 Normal rim		40p/80p
1967*	495	Wide rim BU 2011		/£2.00 (Predecimal.com)
1970	495A/B.	750,424 Proofs		MV/£4 (Predecimal)

*Total mintage for 1967 Includes 46,226,400 struck in 1968, dated 1967.

1953 - Obv 1: The lower relief head. The cross points between rim beads. Obv 2: Slightly sharper. The Cross points to a rim bead.

1967 - Wide Rim or normal rim:

The illustration above shows both rim types. Without a comparison the difference can be detected by looking at the 'I' in 'DEI'. The wide rim variety 'I' points between two rim beads, with the normal rim coin it points directly at a rim bead.

The top image to the right is the 1957 Calm sea variety. The bottom image is the normal 1957 with choppy sea.

Minor reverse varieties occur for the 1957 calm sea type:
1. The '7' points to a bead. 2. The '7' points to left of bead.
3. The '7' points to space. 4. A blunter '7' that points to a bead.
Number 2 is thought to be the rarest.

From 1770 until the end of the 18th Century the practice of melting down the official copper coins and making lightweight forgeries had become so widespread that it prompted industrialist Matthew Boulton to offer a potential solution. He proposed that each coin should actually be made to contain its value in copper and that the quality should be improved by using a retaining collar during striking (to give a perfectly round coin) and by designing the coins with thick raised borders to prevent them wearing so easily. Conrad Heinrich Küchler was the designer. By 1806 the price of copper had risen, and as a result the second Soho penny type was made of reduced weight. In fact, by the time they were ready, the price of copper had fallen and the intrinsic weight was less than the face value. The public accepted this, and ever since then coins have deliberately been made with an actual metal value less than the face value. It is perhaps a strange coincedence that 200 years later the opposite should happen. A steep rise in the price of copper due to the demand from China and India, has caused the value in existing modern bronze 1p's and 2p's to be worth more than the face value of the coins (only the non magnetic coins). I expect Mr Boulton would find it quite amusing that after 200 years the fluctuations in the price of copper could still make the mintmaster sweat! The value of copper fell during the 'credit crunch', but in early 2011 at the time of writing, a bronze 2p is worth about 2.5p.

George III 1797 Penny

* Varieties for 1797 concern the number of leaves in the Kings headdress.

GEORGE III First Soho 'Cartwheel' type, Copper 36mm. Weight 1oz/28.35g (official)

Date	Peck	Mintage	Fine	VF	EF	UNC/BU
1797	P1132	10 leaves*	£12	£60	£325	£800/
1797	P1133	11 leaves*	£14	£70	£300	

George III 1806 Penny

GEORGE III Second Soho type, Copper 35mm. Weight 18.876g

Date	Peck	Mintage	Fine	VF	EF	UNC/BU
1806	P1342	Type A*	£6	£20	£80	£300/£400
1806	P1343	Type B*	£5	£20	£80	£300/
1807	P1344		£6	£20	£80	£300/£400
1808	P1346	One Known		Spink 1985		£15,000
1808	"		Coincraft 1996			£35,000

* 1806 - Type A (above left) has a small incuse hair curl to the right of the tie knot. Type B (above right) has a slightly different pattern of curls.

George IV 1826 Penny

GEORGE IV Copper 34mm. Weight 18.72g.

Date	Peck	Mintage	Fine	VF	EF	UNC/BU
1825	P1420	1,075,200 Type A	£12	£40	£200	£500/
1826	P1422	5,913,000 Type A	£10	£40	£200	£450/
1826	P1425	Inc above. Type B	£10	£40	£200	£500/
1826	P1427	Inc above. Type C	£12	£50	£200	£500/
1827	P1430	1,451,520 Type A	£150	£500	£3000	

No pennies or halfpennies were issued from 1820 to 1824, and it was only when the new portrait by William Wyon was designed in 1825 (which the king much preferred) that an issue of pennies and halfpennies was made. The reverse was also the work of William Wyon.

Type A

Type B

Type C

The reverse varieties of the 1826 George IV pennies all concern slight differences to the cross of St. Andrew in the flag on the shield:

Rev A = No central line along arms of cross.
Rev B = Thin, raised line along cross.
Rev C = Thick, broad raised line along cross.

With many worn coins these varieties are impossible to differenciate, especially without a comparison.

William IV 1837 Penny

The portrait of King William IV was engraved by William Wyon, from a bust by Sir Francis Chantrey. The reverse was the same as that used for King George IV. Coins were also struck in 1832, 1835 and 1836, but were not dated as such.

WILLIAM IV Copper 34mm. Weight 18.85g

Date	Peck	Mintage	Fine	VF	EF	UNC/BU
1831	P1455	806,400 no WW	£15	£50	£250	£500/£700
1831	ND	WW with no Dots	? Exists			
1831	P1458	.W.W incuse on trunc	£25	£80	£250	£500/£700
1831	P1458	W.W incuse on trunc		£300		
1834	P1459	322,560	£25	£65	£300	£1000/
1837	P1460	174,720	£50	£150	£500	£1500/

trunc = truncation, the base of the monarch's neck.

The copper Victorian pennies were, like the previous, engraved by William Wyon, who was clearly kept quite busy by the relatively frequent change of British monarchs in the first half of the 19th Century. The only change to the reverse was to replace 'REX' with 'REG' (for Regina).

VICTORIA Young Head, date below head, Copper 34mm. Weight 18.82g

Date	Peck	Mintage	Fine	VF	EF	UNC/BU
1841	P1480	913,920 REG:	£10	£20	£140	£400/
1841	P1484	No colon REG	£5	£20	£120	£400/
1843	P1486	483,830 colon REG:	£200			
1843	P1485	No colon REG	£70	£450	£1000	£2000/
1844	P1487	215,040	£8	£20	£100	£350/
1845	P1489	322,560	£40	£200		
1846	P1490	483,840 DEF_:	£30	£100		
1846	P1491	DEF:	£50	£200		
1847	P1492	430,080 DEF:	£7	£25	£100	£350/
1847	P1493	DEF_:	£7	£25	£100	£350/
1848	P1496	161,280	£7	£25	£100	£350/
1848	P1494	8 over 6	£20	£100	£400	
1848	P1495	8 over 7	£20	£80	£120	£400/
1849	P1497	268,800	£300	£600	£2000	
1851	P1498	432,224 DEF_:	£10	£30	£100	£300/
1851	P1499	DEF:	£14	£25	£120	£400/
1853	P1500	1,021,440 DEF_:	£5	£12	£80	£250/
1853	ND	Narrow date			£100	£300/
1853	P1503	DEF:	£4	£20	£80	£250/
1853	P1504	PT	£20	£35	£100	£350/

VICTORIA Young Head, date below head, Copper 34mm. Weight 18.82g

Date	Peck	Mintage	Fine	VF	EF	UNC/BU
1854	P1505	4 over 3	£15	£50	£200	£400/
1854	P1506	6,720,000 PT	£5	£18	£80	£250/
1854	P1507	OT	£10	£20	£80	£300/
1855	P1508	5,273,866 OT	£5	£15	£80	£250/
1855	P1509	PT	£7	£20	£80	£250/
1856	P1510	1,212,288 DEF: PT	£70	£200	£700	£2000/
1856	P1512	DEF_: OT	£80	£250	£900	£2000/
1857	P1514	752,640 DEF: PT	£8	£25	£100	£300/
1857	P1513	DEF_: OT	£10	£25	£100	£340/
1857	P1514	Smaller date PT	£10	£30	£130	£300/
1858		1,559,040:				
	P1515	2nd 8 over 3		£100	£400	
	ND	2nd 8 over 6			£90	£300/
	P1516	2nd 8 over 7		£15	£100	£350/
	ND	2nd 8 over 9	(noted 2003)			£100/
	P1517	Smaller date	£4	£20	£80	£250/
	P1518	Large date, no W.W.	£4	£20	£80	£250/£300
	ND	Large date over small date. VF: £36 (noted 2008)				
1859	P1519	1,075,200 Large date	£8	£25	£80	£170/
1859	ND	9 over 8	£10	£40	£150	
1859	P1519	Smaller date	£8	£30	£100	£200/
1860*	P1521	60 struck over 59		£1500		

*NOT the date below Britannia, smaller bronze type.

Victoria 1853 Penny

DEF: = near colon
DEF_: = far colon
OT - ornamental trident
PT - plain trident

Plain trident coins have near colons.

From 1839 to 1851 all have Ornamental tridents.

An ornamental trident (right image) is shown in comparison to a Plain trident (left image). Notice the extra garnishing under the main prongs of the ornamental trident.

The images above also illustrate a near colon after DEF and the far colon (right image)

The 'Bun' Penny

Copper, when alloyed with small quantities of tin and zinc produces bronze, which is a tougher metal. This metal was used to produce british 'coppers' from 1860 onwards. The dies of these lighter, smaller pennies were engraved by Leonard Charles Wyon, a son of William Wyon, who was clearly born to take over from his father (he was actually born on the Royal Mint premises in 1826).

The early bun head series is probably the most complicated coin series ever! As you can see, there are 17 different types for the circulation 1860 coin alone. Correct identification can be a problem with coins in lower grades. Illustrations of every single type would be beyond the scope of this book and readers are refered to 'The British Bronze Penny - Struck for use as currency 1860 - 1970' by Michael Gouby. The book is available on his website: www.michaelcoins.co.uk

The reverse type letters are strictly those specified by Freeman in 'The Bronze Coinage of Great Britain". Here is a brief outline of the major reverse types:

Reverse A = The crosses are outlined by close, double raised lines, Britannia's thumb does not touch cross. no rock to left of lighthouse. **Reverse B** = The crosses are outlined with treble incuse lines, Britannia's thumb touches cross of St. George, no rock to left of lighthouse. **Reverse C** = Similar to Rev. A, but cross outlines are thinner and wider apart. Small rock to the left of lighthouse. **Reverse D** = As Reverse C, but with minor modifications to rocks and sea and, of course, a toothed border. **Reverse E** = As Reverse D, but with L.C.W. incuse below the foot, and the rim of the shield is thicker. **Reverse F** = No L.C.W signature and a rounded top to the lighthouse. Reverse G = No L.C.W signature. The shield is slightly convex (all previous types are flat). Where the letter 'H' appears in the listings after the date, it indicates a Heaton mint coin, distinguished by a small 'H' under date of the coin.

Victoria 1862 Penny
in fairly low grade

The varieties and design of the Bronze Victorian pennies are described in exquisite detail, by Michael J. Freeman in his book 'The Bronze Coinage of Great Britain' and by Michael Gouby in his book 'The British Bronze Penny - Struck for use as Currency 1860 - 1970'.

Above is Reverse A. Note the double raised lines outlining the crosses and that Britannia's thumb doesn't touch the cross.

Reverse B. Note the treble raised lines outlining the crosses and that Britannia's thumb does touch the cross.

VICTORIA Bun Head, date below Britannia, Bronze 30.81mm. Weight 9.442g
1860 Bronze Penny. Mintage: 5,053,440
Beaded rim (T1), Obverse: 'L.C.WYON' partly on truncation

Rev	FMAN	Mintage	Fine	VF	EF	UNC/BU
A	1		£80	£300	£900	
A	ND	extra heavy flan (probably a proof)			£1000	
B	6		£40	£100	£220	£500/
C	7		£100		£500	£1200
Mule	8	bead obv/tooth rev. Fine: £1100. GEF £2900				
Mule	9	tooth obv/bead rev. Fine: £700. EF w/lustre £2700				
D	13	signature below shield		£20	£200	£400/
E	14	signature below foot		£200	£700	£1200/
D	10	signature below shield		£15	£80	£250/
D	ND	N of ONE over sideways N			£500	£1000/
D	ND	struck on heavy flan		£300		
D	15	signature below truncation		£20	£100	£250/
D	16	no signature 15 leaves		£50	£200	£500/
D	17	no signature 16 leaves		£50	£250	£600/
D	ND	ONF PENNY variety: damaged 'E':				
			£20	£90	£250	£400/
	ND	Michael Gouby '1860T' (see bibliography) Fine: £200				
	ND	E over P in PENNY. Fine: £950. Only 1 known.				
1861 Mintage: 36,449,280						
D	18	Signature	£60	£250	£600	
F	20	No signature	£50	£150	£500	
D	21	LCW almost touches border, see Freeman. EF: £5500				
D	22	Signature below	£7	£20	£80	£200/£300
G	25	No signature	£200			
D	26	No signature, 15 leaves	£25	£100	£300	
D	29	No signature, 16 leaves	£10	£40	£150	£300/
G	33	6 over 8	£700			
G	33	No signature	£7	£25	£80	£200/

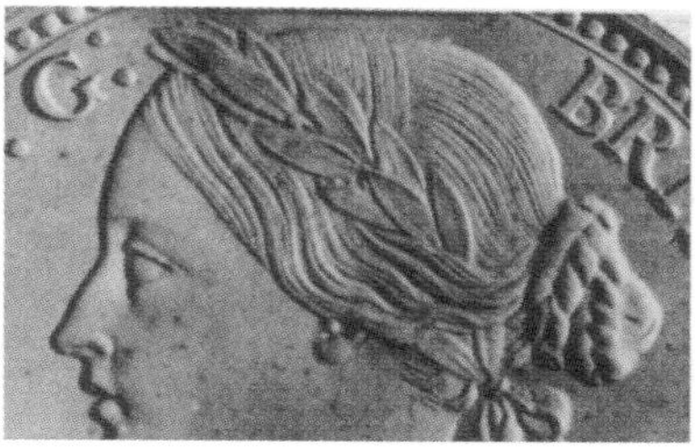

Above is the obverse type with 15 leaves (and 4 berries). When counting, use a good lens and don't forget the leaves below the strands of hair which are swept over the ear!

Reverse C. Very similar to Reverse A but with small rock to left of the lighthouse.

VICTORIA Bun Head, date below Britannia, Bronze 30.81mm (continued)

Date	FMAN	Mintage	Fine	VF	EF	UNC/BU
1862	38	With signature (refer to Freeman, see bibliography)				£4000/
1862	ND	2 of date over 1	Near Fine: £1050			
1862	39	50,534,400	£2	£15	£65	£200/
1862	41	Date from halfpenny die (smaller): Good Fine: £1600 (Bamford 2006)				
1862	39A	8 over 6			£1500	£2000/
1863	42	28,062,720	£2	£15	£65	£200/
1863	45	'2' below date		£4000 (Bamford 2006)		
1863	46	'3' below date	£2400 (Bamford 2006)			
1863	47	'4' below date	Good: £2000 (Bamford 2006)			
1863	ND	'5' below date, only one known. Very very worn: £18,000				
1863	ND	'3' with shorter lower serif in date.			£1350 (Bamford 2006)	
(See book: 'The British Bronze Penny'. More details in bibliography section.)						
1864*	49	3,440,646, Type A	£40	£100	£600	£2000
1864*	48	Inc above. Type B			£1250 (Bamford 2006)	
1865	50	8,601,600	£7	£30	£100	£400/
1865	51	5 over 3	£40	£150	£600	£1100/
1866	52	9,999,360	£15	£30	£75	£300/
1867	53	5,483,520	£12	£70	£250	£460/
1868	56	1,182,720	£12	£70	£250	£460/
1869	59	2,580,480	£180	£450	£1500	£3000/
1870	60	5,695,022	£7	£30	£90	£340/
1870	ND	Narrower date			£250	
1871	61	1,290,318	£60	£200	£400	£1000/
1872	62	8,494,572	£7	£25	£100	£210/
1873	63	8,494,200	£7	£25	£70	£180/
1874		4 varieties. Freeman 65, 67, 70 and 72. Valuations similar.				
		5,621,865	£12	£50	£160	£380/£450
1874H		4 varieties. Freeman 66, 68, 71 and 73.				
		6,666,240	Fine: £12-£30	VF: £50-£100	EF:£150-£300	
1875	80	10,691,040	£10	£60	£350	£840/
1875	82	Wider date, thicker trident			£100	£350/
1875H	85	752,640	£40	£400	£700	£1500/
1876H	87	11,074,560	£8	£30	£200	£350/
1876H	89	Narrow date		£80		£200/
1876H	ND	With missing 'H'	Fair: £230		(Bamford 2006)	
1877	90	Small, narrow date. Fair: £3100 (Bamford 2006)				
1877	91	9,624,747	£6	£20	£100	£200/
1878	94	2,764,470	£8	£25	£100	£300/
1879*	96	7,666,476. Type A	£20	£100	£300	
1879*	97	Inc above. Type B	£4	£15	£90	£200/
1879	98	Small date	£70		£500	
1880*	99	3,000,831	£5	£20	£140	£350/
1881	102	2,302,261	£4	£18	£100	£350/
1881*	106	Portrait 'aged' further			£450	
1881H	108	3,763,200	£4	£20	£100	£280/£500
1882H	111	7,526,400	£4	£16	£100	£300/
1882H	ND	2 over 1			£350	
1882	112	No H*	£820 (Bamford 2006)			

* 1864 types A and B concern the '4' in the date. Type A '4's have an upper pointing serif coming off the right side of the horizontal crossbar of the '4'. Type B '4's have a 'T' shaped end on the horizontal part of the '4'.

*1879 Type A/B pennies have minor obverse differences. One of the easiest to spot (on higher grade coins) is that Type B has double incuse lines for leaf veins, whereas Type A has just a single line.

*1880 Pennies either have rocks to the left of the lighthouse, or not. The image above shows rocks. Values are the same.

*The aged portrait of 1881 is difficult to spot with worn coins, the easiest method is to count the leaves in the wreath - the aged portrait has 15, the normal version has 17.

*There are two 1883 varieties (FMAN 116 and 118) but most dealers do not distinguish. The easiest way to tell the difference is one has the 'RI' of BRITT joined at the bottom, the other doesn't.

• Beware of 1882H coins so worn that the 'H' is worn away, and of coins that have had the 'H' delibrately removed.

VICTORIA Bun Head, date below Britannia, Bronze 30.81mm (continued)

Date	FMAN	Mintage	Fine	VF	EF	UNC/BU
1883*	116/8	6,237,438	£6	£15	£40	£160/
1884	119	11,702,802	£3	£10	£40	£160/£200
1885	121	7,145,862	£3	£10	£40	£160/
1886	123	6,087,759	£3	£10	£40	£160/
1887	125	5,315,085	£4	£15	£60	£160/
1888	126	5,125,020	£5	£20	£50	£170/£250
1889	127	12,559,737 15 leaves	£5	£15	£45	£160/
1889	128	Narrow date 14 leaves in wreath			£75	£300/
1890	130	15,330,840	£3	£12	£50	£160/£200
1890	ND	Narrow date		£200		
1891	132	17,885,961	£2	£10	£40	£160/
1891	ND	Wide spaced date				£340/
1892	134	10,501,671	£2	£10	£40	£160/
1892	ND	Narrow spaced date. Fair: £15				
1893	136	8,161,737	£2	£10	£40	£160/
1894	138	3,883,452	£6	£20	£50	£200/

Dies were engraved by George William de Saulles for the veiled head final victoria issue. The obverse was copied from a model by Thomas Brock, and the reverse was a modified version of the Leonard Charles Wyon type.

VICTORIA Old or Widow Head, Bronze 30.81mm. Weight 9.467g

Date	FMAN	Mintage	Fine	VF	EF	UNC/BU
1895	141	5,395,830 Rev B		£4	£25	£80/
1895*	139	Rev A	£30	£150	£500	
1896	143	24,147,156	£1	£5	£20	£50/£70
1897	145	20,756,620	£1	£3	£20	£50/
1897	147	Spot between O and N in ONE				£1000/
1897*	148	Higher tide			£200	£600/
1898	149	14,296,836	£1	£6	£30	£70/
1899	150	26,441,069	£1	£4	£25	£60/
1900	153	31,778,109		£5	£20	£35/£60
1901	154	22,205,568		£2	£14	£30/£40

1895 - Rev A: trident to the 'P' is 2mm. No sea behind Britannia and to the right of Britannia the tide is very low (see image above).

Rev B: trident to P is 1mm. Sea present behind (to left of) Britannia and the tide level to the right is higher.

Victoria Penny 1901

1897 - Right: The higher tide meets Britannia well above the hemline. The normal tide coin is illustrated.

Right: Many Veiled head pennies have wider spaced dates. Sometimes a premium for extra-wide or very narrow spacing can be added to the value.

The dies for this issue were also by George William de Saulles ('De S' can be seen beneath the bust). Pennies struck early in 1902 used the same reverse as the veiled head Victoria issue. This die was slightly changed during 1902, resulting in the low tide, and normal tide types.

EDWARD VII Bronze 30.81mm. Weight 9.435g

Date	FMAN	Mintage	Fine	VF	EF	UNC/BU
1902	156	Low tide	£6	£30	£100	£200/
		Minor date pointing varieties occur for the above.				
1902	157	26,976,768	£1	£3	£15	£50/£70
1903	158	21,415,296		£4	£20	£70/£90
1903	158A	Open '3' (bottom serif points at the '0')				
			£100 (not seen better than GF)			
1904	159	12,913,152		£8	£40	£100/£150
1905*	160/1	17,783,808		£5	£30	£90/
1906	162	37,989,504		£4	£20	£70/
1907	163	47,322,240		£4	£20	£70/
1908*	164-6	31,506,048		£5	£20	£70/
1909	168	19,617,024 '1' right of tooth			£20	£70/
1909	169	'1' is directly above tooth				£2000/
1910	170	29,549,184		£4	£20	£70/

*1905 FMAN 160 and 161 either have upright part of the 'E' in 'PENNY' pointing at a rim bead or at a gap.

*1908 FMAN 164, 164A, 165 and 166 - Four slight varieties, most are common with the exception of 164A which has the colon after BRITT pointing to a rim tooth. This variety is rare.

Edward Penny 1902

The image above shows the 1902 low tide type; the tide is about level with the hemline. The image below shows the 1902 penny normal tide, which is higher and roughly level with where the legs cross.

George V 1912 H Penny.
Large (first) head obverse.

The BM initials on the truncation of George V stand for Bertram Mackennal, the designer of the George V bust. The first reverse type was identical to that used for Edward VII. There were big problems with 'ghosting' (see also George V Half penny notes) for this issue throughout most of the reign. Despite the head being modified in 1926 and some changes to the reverse, this problem was not completely solved until the issue of the smaller head type in 1928. The 1912, 1918 and 1919 H / KN pennies have the mintmark to the left of the date. Some 1912H pennies are 1/10 mm greater in diameter.

GEORGE V Bronze 30.81mm . Weight 9.45g

Date	FMAN	Mintage	Fine	VF	EF	UNC/BU
1911	171	23,079,168		£3	£20	£50/£60
1912	172	48,306,048		£3	£20	£60/
1912H	173	16,800,000		£12	£100	£200/
1913*	174-7	65,497,872		£5	£35	£70/
1914	178	50,820,997		£3	£20	£50/
1915	179	47,310,807		£3	£20	£50/
1915 and 1916 with ear recessed, add approx 20%						
1916	180	86,411,165		£2	£20	£50/
1917	181	107,905,436		£2	£20	£50/
1918	182	84,227,372		£2	£20	£50/
1918H	183	3,660,800	£3	£25	£200	£500/
1918KN	184		£15	£90	£400	£600/
1919	185	113,761,090		£2	£20	£50/
1919H	186	5,209,600	£5	£50	£300	£700/
1919KN	187	Inc above	£20	£100	£500	£1000/
1920	188	124,693,485		£2	£20	£50/
1920	189	Colon after IMP points at a tooth. Ext. rare.				
1921*	190/1	129,717,693		£2	£20	£50/£60
1922	192	16,346,711		£3	£25	£40/£50
1922	192A	Centre trident prong well below tooth. Fine: £1200 (2006)				
1926	193	4,498,519		£20	£80	£170/
1926	195	Modified effigy, see app I	£40	£200	£1000	
1927	197	60,989,561		£2	£15	£40/
1928	199	50,178.000		£2	£15	£40/
1929	201	49,132,800		£1	£15	£30/
1930	203	29,097,600		£2	£20	£30/£40
1931	205	19,843,200		£2	£15	£40/£50
1932	207	8,277,600		£3	£30	£70/£100
1933*		7 or 8+ 'patterns'	£45,000 (2006)			
1933*		Pattern by Lavrillier £4,100 (1986)				
1933*		A uniface £28,750 (1980)		£40,000+ (estimated)		
1933*		Modern reproduction 'patterns' are plentiful.				£20/£25
1934	210	13,965,600		£2	£20	£40/£50
1935	212	56,070,000		£1	£5	£10/£20
1936	214	154,296,000		£1	£3	£8/£15

*1913 - Four minor varieties, all are fairly common and distinguishing them depends on the pointing of the 'P' on the reverse, and the position of the colon between 'GRA : BRITT'.

*1921 FMAN 190 and 191 - Two varieties occur, they can be differentiated by looking at the colon after 'DEF'. The 190 colon points to a gap, the 191 colon points to a tooth. Values are about the same.

*1933 Pennies shouldn't really be listed in the circulated coins area because none were struck for circulation. I thought I'd keep it here for completeness as it's certainly one of those legendary British coins.

George V 1935 Penny

George V 1933 Pattern Penny. Struck at the Royal Mint with dies by Frenchman André Lavrillier. It is thought there are only 4 in existance. The coin shown here is from the British Museum collection.

EDWARD VIII Bronze 30.81mm

Date	FMAN	Mintage	VF	EF	UNC/BU
1937	Specimen strikings only, from				£40,000

Edward VIII Penny from the British Museum Collection.

GEORGE VI Bronze 30.81mm. Weight 9.442g

The obverse was engraved from a model by Thomas Humphrey Paget and the reverse was a slightly different Britannia type, modified by Royal Mint staff. During the war tin became scarce, so the percentage in the bronze alloy was reduced from 3% to 0.5%. The coins dated 1944 - 46 were also chemically darkened to give them the same tones as the previous un-treated coins. For all George VI coins, the titles IND:IMP were removed in 1949.

Date	FMAN	Mintage	Fine	VF	EF	UNC/BU
1937*	217/9	88,896,000			£1	£3/£8
1937*	218/20	26,402 Proofs			£3	£10/£15
1938	222	121,560,000			£1	£10/£15
1939	224	55,560,000			£2	£15/£25
1940	226	42,284,400		£3	£10	£30/£35
1940*	227	Double exergue line			£5	£10/£20
1944*	229	42,600,000			£3	£10/£20
1944*	ND	Not darkened by Mint				£20/£30
1945	231	79,531,200		£1	£5	£18/
1945	ND	Doubled 9		£5	£25	
1946	233	66,355,600			£2	£8/£10
1947	235	52,220,400			£1	£4/£6
1948	236	63,961,200			£1	£3/£6
1949	238	14,324,400			£1	£4/£7
1950	240	240,000	£3	£8	£18	£50/£60
1950	241	17,513 Proofs			FDC	£30
1951	242	120,000	£3	£8	£25	£50/£60
1951	243	20,000 Proofs			FDC	£35
1952		(2006 Rasmussen)				£37,500

*1937 FMAN 217 and 219 - Two varieties occur with alternate pointings for the 2nd upright of the 'N' in 'ONE'. Both are fairly common and the same varieties are also found in the proof 1937 Pennies, FMAN 218 and 220.

*1940 FMAN 227. Below is an example of the double exergue 1940 penny

*1944 FMAN 229 - Unconfirmed sightings of a 1944 penny with the waves reaching slightly into the exergue.

George VI Penny first obverse with IND IMP.

George VI 1951 Penny

ELIZABETH II Bronze 30.81mm. Weight 9.396g

Date	FMAN	Mintage	EF	BU
1953*	245	1,308,400	£3	£10
1953	246	40,000 Proofs		£18
1954		1 retrieved from change. Now in British Museum.		
1954		Another (2006 Rasmussen) £37,500		
1961	248	48,313,400		£3
1962	250	157,588,600		£2
1963	252	119,733,600		£2
1964	254	153,294,000		£1
1965	255	121,310,400		£1
1966	256	165,739,200		£1
1967	257	654,564,000**		50p
1970	257A	750,424 Proofs from the set		£6

* 1953 non proof pennies were only issued originally in the 9 coin plastic sets.
** 1967 Mintage includes pennies minted in 1968, 69 and 70 but dated 1967.

Elizabeth II 1964 Penny

Three Halfpences or One and a Half pence

These tiny coins were issued for use in some colonies, and were never legal tender in the UK. They are included here because, like the fractional farthings, they are at the very least relatives of the normal British Coinage, and they do bear the latin word 'Britanniar' (Britain). I wonder how many of these tiddlers ended up down the back of sofas, never again to see the light of day.

WILLIAM IV .925 fine Silver 12mm. Weight 0.7g

Date	FMAN	Mintage	Fine	VF	EF	UNC/BU
1834	2250	800,448	£6	£15	£40	£80/
1835	2251	633,600	£10	£25	£80	£140/
1835	2251A	5 over 4	£6	£20	£70	£100/
1836	2252	158,400	£5	£15	£40	£90/
1837	2253	30,624	£10	£40	£100	£200/

William IV 1834 Threehalfpence

VICTORIA .925 fine Silver 12mm. Weight 0.7g

Date	FMAN	Mintage	Fine	VF	EF	UNC/BU
1838	2254	538,560	£6	£12	£30	£65/
1839	2255	760,320	£4	£12	£30	£65/
1840	2256	95,040	£8	£20	£70	£120/
1841	2257	158,400	£6	£15	£40	£90/
1842	2258	1,869,120	£4	£14	£40	£80/
1843	2259	475,200	£4	£12	£30	£60/
1843	2259B	43/34	£10	£30	£100	£180/
1860	2260	160,000	£5	£20	£60	£90/
1862	2261	256,000	£5	£20	£60	£100/

Victoria 1839 Threehalfpence

Cartwheel Twopence

The heaviest British regal coin ever circulated, Cartwheel twopences are 41mm in diameter, over 5mm thick, and weigh almost 60 grammes each. With the Cartwheel Penny (see penny section) these two coins were the first to be struck for circulation by the new steam powered presses installed by James Watt at the premises of Matthew Boulton in Soho, Birmingham. Those two men changed the shape (quite literally!) of British coinage and set the standard for all coins that followed. The fact they are such heavy coins means they are more likely to show signs of edge damage. Serious, or multiple edge knocks will result in lower values.

GEORGE III Copper 41mm. Weight 2oz/56.7g (official)

Date	Peck	Mintage	Fine	VF	EF	UNC/BU
1797	P1077	722,160	£30	£70	£200	£700/

George III Cartwheel Twopence

LINDNER *Das Original*

Solid Wood Case Premium

Pure wood case containing 3 wooden trays with recess to enable easy removal from case. Several different combinations of red inserts, which are compatible with the standard Lindner coin boxes, are available.

Item 2493-1 Wood Case & 3 trays, 1 each 48, 25 & 20 compartments

Price £54.50

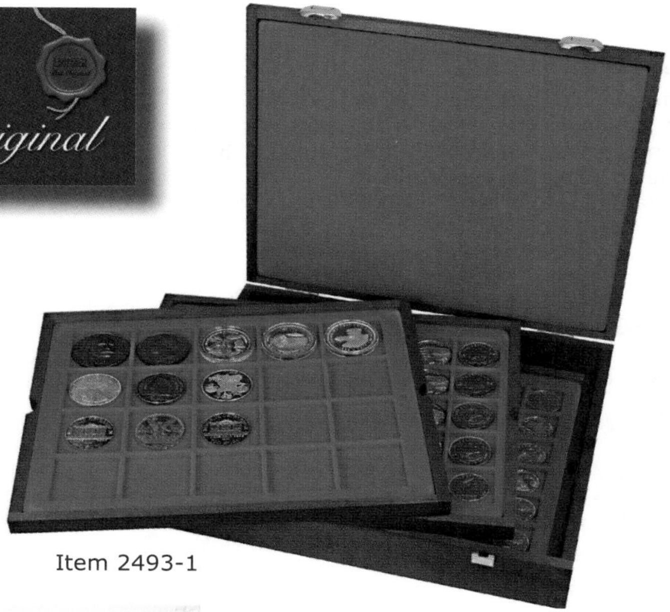

Item 2493-1

REBECK L Coin Holders

Self adhesive coin holders with extra space for writing on. Can be used in landscape or portrait format. Overall size of each coin holder 50mm x 70mm. Available in the following sizes
17.5 mm, 20.0 mm
22.5 mm, 25.0 mm
27.5 mm, 30.0 mm
32.5 mm, 35.0 mm
37.5 mm, 39.5 mm

Price £3.26

REBECK L Coin Holder Storage Cases

Specially made for the Rebeck L coin holders these solid wood boxes, fitted with brass latches, have a detachable lid making scrolling through.

Small box to hold 80-100 coin holders, overall size 295mm x 60mm x 80mm Single compartment with 1 fixed and 1 movable wooden wedge.Ref RCB1 £8.48

Large box to hold 400-500 coin holders, overall size 235mm x 300mm x 80mm Five compartments supplied with 1 fixed and 5 movable wooden wedges.
Ref RCB2 £19.20

Threepences

Later George III, all George IV and early William IV Threepences:
At some point in the late 1700s/early 1800s (the jury is still out on exactly when) the threepence stopped being a circulating coin minted in large numbers, and was only minted for use in the annual Maundy ceremony. The circulation of a currency threepence for use in the United Kingdon was re-started in the early part of Queen Victoria's reign. For this reason, the threepences dated between 1800 - 1833 can be found in the Maundy section.

WILLIAM IV .925 fine Silver 16mm. Weight 1.414g

Date	ESC	Details	Fine	VF	EF	UNC/BU
1831-1833 - Maundy type only see Maundy section.						
1834	2044	401,016	£7	£20	£60	£150/
1835	2045	491,040	£7	£20	£70	£160/
1836	2046	411,840	£7	£20	£70	£160/
1837	2047	42,768	£10	£25	£80	£180/

All the non-Maundy William IV threepences listed here were only issued for use in the West Indies. They do not have a prooflike mirror finish like the Maundy threepences.

VICTORIA .925 fine Silver 16mm.. Weight 1.414g

Young Head, as Maundy type but without prooflike mirrored surface. The bust was changed slightly in 1859, 1867 and 1880, although some later coins were struck using earlier dies. A comprehensive listing of the four obverse types and two different reverses is given in 'English Silver Coins' by P Alan Rayner.

Date	ESC	Details	Fine	VF	EF	UNC/BU
1838*	2048	1,203,840	£7	£18	£70	£150/
1838*	2048A	BRITANNIAB error			Extremely rare	
1839*	2049	570,240	£8	£20	£80	£150/£175
1840*	2050	633,600	£7	£20	£80	£150/
1841*	2051	443,520	£7	£28	£80	£180/
1842*	2052	2,027,520	£8	£20	£80	£150/
1843*	2053	Inc above	£7	£20	£80	£150/
1844*	2054	1,045,400	£5	£20	£80	£130/
1845	2055	1,314,720	£8	£20	£60	£120/
1846	2056	47,520	£15	£40	£120	£250/
1847*	ND	Unknown			£375	
1848*	2056A	Unknown	£50	£150	£350	
1849	2057	126,720	£8	£20	£80	£140/
1850	2058	950,400	£7	£15	£70	£125/
1851	2059	479,065	£8	£15	£70	£140/
1851	2059A	5/8	£15	£40	£80	£150/
1852*	2059B		£60	£200	£450	£950/
1853	2060	31,680	£20	£40	£140	£250/
1854	2061	1,467,246	£7	£18	£70	£150/
1855	2062	383,350	£8	£25	£80	£175/
1856	2063	1,013,760	£8	£25	£80	£175/
1857	2064	1,758,240	£8	£25	£80	£175/
1858	2065	1,441,440	£7	£15	£60	£100/
1858	2065A	BRITANNIAB	£40	£150	£300	
1859	2066	3,579,840	£7	£15	£60	£110/
1860	2067	3,405,600	£7	£15	£60	£110/
1861	2068	3,294,720	£7	£15	£60	£120/
1862	2069	1,156,320	£10	£20	£70	£120/
1863	2070	950,400	£10	£25	£80	£150/
1864	2071	1,330,560	£7	£15	£60	£110/
1865	2072	1,742,400	£7	£20	£70	£140/

Victoria Threepence 1864

Coins marked with an asterix were intended for colonial use only.

VICTORIA .925 fine Silver 16mm.. Weight 1.414g [continued]

Date	ESC	Details	Fine	VF	EF	UNC/BU
1866	2073	1,900,800	£7	£15	£60	£110/
1866	2073	1,900,800	£7	£15	£60	£110/
1867	2074	712,800	£7	£15	£60	£110/
1868	2075	1,457,280	£7	£15	£60	£110/
1868	2075A	RRITANNIAR	£70	£150		
1869	2075C	4,488 Maundy Only	£10	£25	£75	£120/
1870	2076	1,283,218	£5	£15	£50	£80/£100
1871	2077	999,633	£5	£15	£50	£80/£100
1872	2078	1,293,271	£10	£20	£60	£120/
1873	2079	4,055,550	£5	£12	£45	£80/£100
1874	2080	4,427,031	£5	£12	£45	£80/£100
1875	2081	3,306,500	£5	£12	£45	£60/£100
1876	2082	1,834,389	£5	£10	£45	£85/
1877	2083	2,622,393	£8	£15	£45	£85/
1878	2084	2,419,975	£10	£20	£50	£85/
1879	2085	3,140,265	£9	£15	£50	£85/
1880	2087	1,610,069	£6	£10	£40	£80/
1881	2088	3,248,265	£4	£9	£30	£70/
1882	2089	472,965	£10	£25	£70	£120/
1883	2090	4,365,971	£4	£10	£30	£70/
1884	2091	3,322,424	£5	£10	£35	£65/
1885	2092	5,183,653	£4	£10	£30	£60/£80
1886	2093	6,152,669	£4	£9	£30	£60/£80
1887	2094	2,780,761	£4	£10	£40	£75/

Victoria Young Head 1878 Threepence

The controversial Jubilee head bust (some people have remarked that it made the Queen look like a penguin, with a ridiculously small crown) was designed by Joseph Edgar Boehm.

VICTORIA .925 fine Silver 16mm Jubilee head (JH). Weight 1.414g

Date	ESC	Details	Fine	VF	EF	UNC/BU
1887	2096	Inc above	£2	£4	£6	£15/£20
1887	2097	Proof				/£70
1888	2098	518,199	£5	£10	£18	£45/
1889	2099	4,587,010	£2	£4	£15	£30/
1890	2100	4,465,834	£2	£4	£15	£30/
1891	2101	6,323,027	£2	£4	£15	£30/
1892	2102	2,578,226	£2	£5	£15	£30/
1893	2103	3,067,243	£14	£50	£120	£250/

Victoria Jubilee Head 1887 Threepence

Dies were engraved by George William de Saulles for the veiled head final victoria issue. The obverse was copied from a model by Thomas Brock.

VICTORIA .925 fine Silver 16mm Old, or Widow head. Weight 1.414g

Date	ESC	Details	Fine	VF	EF	UNC/BU
1893	2104	Inc with JH	£2	£5	£10	£20/£30
1893	2105	1,312 Proofs				/£90
1894	2106	1,608,603	£3	£5	£18	£36/
1895	2107	4,788,609	£3	£5	£12	£22/
1896	2108	4,598,442	£3	£5	£12	£22/
1897	2109	4,541,294	£2	£4	£12	£22/
1898	2110	4,567,177	£2	£4	£12	£22/
1899	2111	6,246,281	£2	£4	£12	£22/
1900	2112	10,644,480	£2	£3	£10	£20/
1901	2113	6,098,400	£1	£4	£8	£22/

Victoria Veiled Head 1898 Threepence

EDWARD VII .925 fine Silver 16mm. Weight 1.414g

George William de Saulles engraved the Edward VII bust.

Date	ESC	Mintage	Fine	VF	EF	UNC/BU
1902	2114	8,268,480	£1	£2	£10	£15/£20
1902	2115	15,123 Proofs				£15/£25
1903	2116	5,227,200	£3	£8	£30	£40/£50
1904	2117	3,627,360	£6	£9	£35	£80/
1905	2118	3,548,160	£7	£11	£50	
1906	2119	3,152,160	£3	£8	£20	£40/£45
1907	2120	4,831,200	£2	£5	£10	£25/£30
1908	2121	8,157,600	£2	£5	£12	£25/£35
1909	2122	4,055,040	£2	£8	£20	£40/
1910	2123	4,563,380	£1	£4	£12	£30/

Edward VII Threepence obverse. Reverse type was as the early Geroge V Threepence (below)

GEORGE V .925 fine Silver 16mm. Weight 1.414g

The bust was by Bertram MacKennal, the reverse was carried over from the previous type until the acorn type was adopted in 1927, and ran to the end of the reign.

George V Threepence 1920

Date	ESC	Mintage	Fine	VF	EF	UNC/BU
1911	2124	5,841,084	BV	£2	£7	£18/£25
1911	2125	6,001 Proofs				£20/
1912	2126	8,932,825	BV	£3	£9	£15/£20
1913	2127	7,143,242	£1	£4	£7	£20/£30
1914	2128	6,733,584	BV	£2	£6	£20/£25
1915	2129	5,450,617	BV	£2	£6	£20/£25
1916	2130	18,555,201	BV	£1	£4	£20/£25
1917	2131	21,662,490	BV	£1	£4	£20/£25
1918	2132	20,630,909	BV	£1	£4	£20/£25
1919	2133	16,845,687	BV	£1	£4	£20/£25
1920*	2134	16,703,597		£2	£6	£25/
Now debased .500 (50%) silver, type and size as previous.						
1920*	2135	.500 silver		£1	£5	£20/
1921	2136	8,749,301	£1	£3	£9	£25/
1922	2137	7,979,998	£1	£2	£20	£40/£70
1925	2138	3,731,859	£1	£5	£10	£30/£40
1926	2139	4,107,910	£1	£4	£30	£80/£100
1926	2140	Modified Effigy (Appedix I)		£4	£8	£20/£30
1927	2141	15,022 Proofs			£50	£70/£90
1928	2142	1,302,106	£1	£4	£12	£28/£40
1930	2143	1,319,412	£2	£5	£15	£28/£40
1931	2144	6,251,936		£1	£5	£10/£14
1932	2145	5,887,325		£1	£5	£10/£14
1933	2146	5,578,541		£1	£3	£10/£12
1934	2147	7,405,954		£1	£2	£8/£10
1935	2148	7,027,654		£1	£2	£7/£9
1936	2149	3,238,670		£1	£2	£7/£9

* Sterling silver 1920 threepences have slightly stronger details, particularly on the serifs of the 'E's, owing to a slight difference in the resistance of the different alloys. Very difficult to spot, and good magnification is needed. Many dealers don't bother, as both are worth about the same.

George V Threepence, 2nd Reverse type (1927-1936)

EDWARD VIII

Date	ESC	Mintage	Fine	VF	EF	UNC/BU
1937	2149D	Pattern, 3 rings on reverse.		expensive!		

GEORGE VI .500 fine Silver 16mm. Weight 1.414g

New reverses were used for nearly all the George VI denominations. The silver threepence featured a St George's cross on a Tudor rose and was designed by George Kruger Gray, whose initials can be seen on many of the George VI reverses. The portrait was by Thomas Humphrey Paget.

Date	ESC	Mintage	Fine	VF	EF	UNC/BU
1937	2150	8,148,156			£2	£6/£7
1937	2151	26,402 Proofs				£8/£10
1938	2152	6,402,473			£3	£10/£12
1939	2153	1,355,860			£4	£14/
1940	2154	7,914,401			£3	£12/
1941	2155	7,979,411			£4	£16/
1942*	2156	4,144,051	£1	£6	£14	£30/
1943*	2157	1,379,220	£2	£5	£15	£40/
1944*	2158	2,005,553	£3	£10	£30	£70/
1945	2159	371,000	(1997: VF £4000)			

Most 1945 coins were melted down.
*For Colonial use only.

George VI Silver 1943 Threepence

Threepences dodecagonal (12 sided) nickel-brass

EDWARD VIII

Officially, no coins bearing the portrait of Edward VIII were issued for circulation despite the fact that all the dies were prepared for all the denominations, and proofs were struck for approval. However, the brass threepence, being a new size and type was produced in slightly higher numbers, primarily for testing in vending machines. A handful of these coins were sent to vending machine manufacturers, and not all were returned! The obverse portrait was by Thomas Humprey Paget and the reverse Thrift plant by Madge Kitchener. Normal thickness, and thinner varieties of this extremely rare coin are known to exist.

Date	Peck		UNC/BU
1937	2365/6	Date divided by THRIFT PLANT (Sea-pink); thicknesses vary. Cooke (1994)	£24,500
1937	2366	As George VI type but effigy of Edward VIII. Coincraft (1999)	£20,000

A current estimate would perhaps be £40,000+ for any type Edward VIII threepence.

Edward VIII Brass 1937 Threepence

GEORGE VI Nickel-brass, 12 sided, 21mm. 6.8g

A modified version of the intended Edward VIII reverse was used for the brass threepences of George VI. At first they were issued simultaneously with the usual small silver type of threepence. Within a few years the silver type was phased out and the twelve sided (dodecagonal) thick brass threepence was struck until 1967 (and in 1970 for the proof set). Early on, the Royal Mint found that the twelve sided collar placed around each coin before striking was prone to weaknesses, especially in the twelve sharp corners. During WWII the quantity of steel available for making these collars declined so in order to make the collars last longer, they were re-made with blunter corners. This experimentation led to a couple of the dates being struck with either sharp or rounded corners. See box below for more details.

Date	Peck	Mintage	Fine	VF	EF	UNC/BU
1937*	2370	45,707,957			£1	£3/£5
1937	2371	26,402 Proofs			£3	£9/£15
1938	2372	14,532,332			£5	£22/£28
1939	2374	5,603,021			£4	£30/£35
1940	2376	12,636,018			£6	£20/£25
1941**	2378/2379A	60,239,489			£2	£9/£10
1942	2380	103,214,400			£2	£9/£10
1943	2382	101,702,400			£2	£9/£10
1944	2384	69,760,000			£2	£10/£12
1945	2386	33,942,466			£3	£14/£20
1946	2388	620,734	£10	£50	£200	
1948**	2390/1	4,230,400			£14	£35/£50
1949	2392	464,000	£6	£50	£150	
1950	2394	1,600,000			£18	£60/£90
1950	2395	17,513 Proofs				£20/£40
1951	2396	1,184,000			£18	£70/£100
1951	2397	20,000 Proofs				£20/£40
1952	2398	25,494,400			£3	£12/£16

George VI Brass 1937 Threepence

*1937 - Two different spacings from rim to word THREE noted. They are not normally distinguished between.

**Sharp and rounded corners: Varieties of George VI threepences exist with either sharp or rounded corners.

1937 - 1940: All Sharp
1941: Sharp or Rounded.
1942 - 1946: All Rounded
1948: Sharp or Rounded
1949: All Rounded
1950 - 1952: All Sharp

ELIZABETH II Nickel-brass, 12 sided. Size/Weight as GVI

William Gardner designed the new portcullis reverse for the brass threepences of Elizabeth II. Mary Gillick was responsible for the young (first) Elizabeth II effigy.

Date	Peck	Mintage	UNC/BU
1953*	2489	30,618,000. Obv 1	£2/£4
1953*	2490	Inc above. Obv 2	£4/£6
1953*	2491	40,000 Proofs	£4/£6
1954	2492	41,720,000	£6/£7
1955	2494	41,075,200	£6/£7
1956	2496	36,801,600	£7/£8
1957	2498	24,294,400	£6/£7
1958	2500	20,504,000	£8/£12
1959	2501A	28,499,200	£5/£6
1960	2501C	83,078,400	£2/£4
1961	2501E	41,102,400	£2/£3
1962	2501G	51,545,600	£1/£2
1963	2501I	35,280,000	£1/£2
1964	ND**	44,867,200	£1/£2
1965	ND**	27,160,000	£1/£2
1966	ND**	53,760,000	60p/£1
1967	ND**	151,780,800	50p/£1
1970	ND**	750,476 Proofs from set	£3/£5
Undated error - double obverse			£375

Elizabeth II Brass 1960 Threepence

*1953 Threepences have 2 distict levels of definition to the Queen's head. The poorly defined Obv 1 type is ex the 1953 specimen set. The sharper Obv 2 is the normal issue, a similar sharper die was also used for the 1953 proofs.

*1953 - Varieties exist with either the I of ELIZABETH pointing to a corner or with it pointing much further to the right.

Fourpences (Groats), non Maundy 'Britannia' type

WILLIAM IV Britannia on reverse .925 fine Silver, 16mm. Weight 1.89g

The William IV Britannia type groats were issued for use in British Guiana to replace the Quarter Guilder. The design and wording is the same as later British issues, and for that reason these coins are included here. Unlike the silver threepence, which is the same size, the Britannia groats have a milled edge.

Date	ESC	Mintage	Fine	VF	EF	UNC/BU
1836	1918	4,253,000	£5	£18	£60	£90/£160
1836	ND	Colons close to D	£10	£40	£100	
1837	1922	962,280	£9	£20	£70	£100/£160

William IV 1836 Groat

VICTORIA Britannia on reverse .925 fine Silver, 16mm. Weight 1.87g

The reverse used for the Young head Victorian Britannia groats was the same as that used previously for William IV. The effigy is that designed by William Wyon.

Victoria 1848 Groat.
The Jubilee Head Groats had the same reverse with the standard Jubilee Head obverse.

Date	ESC	Mintage	Fine	VF	EF	UNC/BU
1838	1930	2,150,280	£6	£12	£50	£100/£150
1838	1931A	2nd 8 struck over sideways 8	£10	£20	£60	£150/£300
1839	1932	1,461,240	£6	£20	£60	£100/£180
1840	1934	1,496,880	£6	£15	£50	£120/£180
1840	1934A	Zero in date rounder, like letter O				
1840	ND	0 (zero) struck over rounder O. Reported 1994.				
1841	1935	344,520	£6	£15	£60	£120/
1841	ND	2nd 1 over upside-down 1		£100		
1842	1936	724,680	£6	£15	£50	£120/£180
1842	1937A	2 struck over 1	£8	£15	£80	
1843	1938	1,817,640	£6	£12	£50	£120/£180
1843	1938A	4 over 5	£10	£25	£60	£150/
1843	ND.	Double 4 in date	£10	£30	(reported 2005)	
1844	1939	855,360	£5	£20	£60	£120/
1845	1940	914,760	£5	£20	£50	£100/
1846	1941	1,366,200	£5	£15	£50	£100/
1847	1942	226,000 7 over 6	£15	£60	£240	
1848	1943	712,800	£5	£10	£50	£100/
1848	1944	2nd 8 over 6	£20	£50	£200	£450/
1848	1944A	2nd 8 over 7	£10	£35	£80	£200/
1849	1945	380,160	£6	£15	£50	£120/
1849	1946	9 over 8	£10	£20	£50	£120/
1851	1947	594,000	£30	£100	£300	£600/
1852	1948	31,300	£50	£200	£550	
1853	1949	11,880	£50	£150	£400	
1854	1952	1,096,613	£5	£10	£40	£100/£150
1854	ND	5 struck over 3	£5	£15	£50	£100/£150
1855	1953	646,041	£5	£10	£40	£100/£150

Jubilee head. Britannia on reverse .925 fine Silver, 16mm. Weight approx 1.87g

The Jubilee head 1888 issue was officially struck only for use in British Guiana. An example was not available at the time of writing to be weighed, so it is assumed that the weight of this coin is about the same as the previous young head issue.

Date	ESC	Mintage	Fine	VF	EF	UNC/BU
1888	1956		£10	£30	£70	£120/£150

GEORGE III .925 Fine Silver, 19mm. Weight 2.827g

The last coinage of George III (from 1816 - 1820) was designed by Benedetto Pistrucci. A big gap exists between sixpences, the previous coins struck for circulation were dated 1787.

Date	ESC	Mintage	Fine	VF	EF	UNC/BU
1816	1630	Inc with 1817	£10	£20	£50	£80/£110
1817	1632	10,921,680	£10	£20	£60	£80/£100
1818	1634	4,284,720	£10	£25	£70	£100/£120
1819	1636	4,712,400	£10	£20	£70	£80/£120
1819	1636A	Very small 8	£10	£20	£65	£80/£120
1819	ND	Noted with full stop after III.				
1820	1638	1,448,960	£10	£20	£60	£100/£120
1820	1639A	Upside-down 1 in date		£200	£500	£1000/

George III 1819 Sixpence

GEORGE IV Laureate first head .925 Fine Silver, 19mm. Weight 2.827g

The first George IV bust was by Benedetto Pistrucci. The reverses of the sixpences of George IV were basically smaller versions of the reverses used for the shillings. The first, used for 1821 only, featured a crowned ornate shield with a large rose under it. The second reverse, used 1824 to 1826 inclusive, featured a squarer shield with a circular garter surrounding it, and no rose beneath. The third reverse, which is only found with the second obverse (the design by William Wyon) was a complete change and features a lion standing on a large crown.

First head with first reverse type.

Date	ESC	Mintage	Fine	VF	EF	UNC/BU
1821	1654	863,280	£10	£35	£100	£250/
1821	1656	BBITANNIAR error	£75	£250	£600	
First head with second reverse type.						
1824	1657	633,600	£10	£20	£140	£300/
1825	1659	483,120	£10	£20	£100	£300/
1826	1660	689,040	£30	£80	£250	£400/
Bare second head with 3rd reverse type.						
1826	1662	Included above	£12	£35	£120	£300/
1827	1664	166,320	£25	£75	£200	£350/
1828	1665	15,840??	£20	£50	£150	£350/
1829	1666	403,920	£12	£35	£120	£300/

George IV 1825 Sixpence
First head with second reverse

The changing reverse types of the George IV sixpences followed the same reverse types as the shillings. The first head was Laureate and very Roman in style, the second head was bare and more contemporary. The first reverse type is the ornate shield with a large crown. The second reverse was a much squarer shield surrounded by a garter (very similar to the Victorian Jubilee shilling reverse). The third reverse type was the large lion standing on a crown.

George IV 1826 Sixpence
Second head with third reverse

WILLIAM IV .925 Fine Silver, 19mm. Weight 2.827g

The William IV sixpences featured the familar William Wyon bust (from a model by Sir Francis Chantrey) and a new wreath type reverse by Jean Baptiste Merlen.

Date	ESC	Mintage	Fine	VF	EF	UNC/BU
1831	1670	1,340,195	£15	£35	£120	£250/
1834*	1674	5,892,480	£15	£35	£120	£250/
1835	1676	1,552,320	£15	£40	£120	£250/
1836	1678	1,987,920	£20	£50	£200	£300/
1837	1680	506,880	£20	£50	£200	£300/

William IV 1831 Sixpence

VICTORIA Young head .925 Fine Silver, 19mm. Weight 3.01g

The young head Victoria portrait, by William Wyon was changed slightly in 1867 and again in 1880. The reverse used was the same as that of William IV, although it was engraved by Leonard Charles Wyon, son of William. Coins dated 1864 to 1879 usually had a tiny die number on the reverse so that the mint staff could check the speed at which the dies became too worn or broken. Usually, what the die number happens to be has no bearing on the value of the coin, although some collectors do try to collect dates by die number.

Date	ESC	Mintage	Fine	VF	EF	UNC/BU
1838	1682	1,607,760	£15	£30	£100	£250/
1839	1684	3,310,560	£15	£30	£100	£250/
1840	1686	2,098,800	£15	£30	£100	£250/
1841	1687	1,386,000	£15	£35	£120	£300/
1842	1688	601,920	£15	£30	£100	£250/
1843	1689	3,160,080	£15	£30	£100	£250/
1844	1690	3,975,840	£12	£30	£100	£250/
1844	1690A	Date has large 44	£20	£35	£120	£300/
1845	1691	3,714,480	£12	£25	£100	£250/
1846	1692	4,268,880	£12	£25	£90	£250/
1847	ND		Extremely rare.			
1848	1693	586,080	£40	£100	£400	£700/
1848	1693A	8 is altered 6	£40	£100	£400	£700/
1848	1693B	8 over 7	£40	£100	£400	£700/
1850	1695	498,960	£12	£25	£90	£250/£300
1850	1695A	5 struck over 3	£20	£40	£150	£400/
1851	1696	2,288,107	£12	£28	£100	£250/£300
1851	ND	Obv has one G with serif, one without. EF: £150				
1852	1697	904,586	£12	£30	£80	£250/£300
1853	ND	53 higher	(noted 2000) £70			
1853	1698	3,837,930	£12	£28	£90	£200/£250
1854	1700	840,116	£100	£300	£700	£1400/£1600
1855	1701	1,129,084	£12	£28	£100	£250/£300
1855	1701A	5 over 3. Slightly rarer than above.				
1856*	1702	2,779,920	£12	£28	£100	£250/£300
1857*	1704	2,233,440	£12	£28	£100	£250/£300
1858	1706	1,932,480	£12	£30	£100	£250/£300
1858	ND	2nd 8 over 6 (London Coins 2007)			£300	
1859	1708	4,688,640	£12	£28	£100	£250/£300

Victoria Young Head 1853 Sixpence

* 1834 - Rarer variety exists with date in large numerals (ESC1674A).

* 1856 and 1857 can also be found with a longer line below the word PENCE (ESC 1703 and 1705 respectively). Both varieties are as common as the normal coins.

VICTORIA Young head .925 Fine Silver, 19mm. Weight 3.01g (continued)

Date	ESC	Mintage	Fine	VF	EF	UNC/BU
1859	1708A	9 struck over 8	£15	£40	£130	
1860	1709	1,100,880	£10	£20	£100	£250/£300
1862	1711	990,000	£50	£150	£400	
1863	1712	491,040	£40	£100	£250	£400/
All Sixpences (except where stated) now have a small die number above the date, until 1879.						
1864	1713	4,253,040	£12	£25	£100	£250/
1865	1714	1,631,520	£12	£25	£100	£250/
1866	1715	5,140,080	£12	£25	£100	£250/
1866	1716	No die number	£500			
1867	1717	1,362,240	£12	£25	£100	£250/£300
1868	1719	1,069,200	£12	£20	£100	£250/£300
1869	1720	388,080	£12	£20	£100	£250/£300
1870	1721	479,613	£12	£20	£100	£250/£300
1871	1723	3,662,684	£12	£20	£80	£200/£250
1871	1724	No die number	£20	£40	£130	£200/£250
1872	1726	3,382,048	£10	£25	£80	£200/£250
1873	1727	4,594,733	£12	£25	£80	£200/£250
1874	1728	4,225,726	£12	£25	£80	£200/
1875	1729	3,256,545	£12	£25	£80	£200/
1876	1730	841,435	£12	£30	£100	£200/£300
1877	1731	4,066,486	£10	£25	£80	£200/£250
1877	1732	No die number	£10	£25	£80	£200/£250
1878	1733	2,624,525	£10	£25	£80	£200/£250
1878	1734A	8 over 7	£50	£120	£280	
1878	ND	8 over 7, no die No.	£50	£150	£300	
1878	1735	DRITANNIAR error	£60	£200	£500	£800/
1879	1736	3,326,313	£10	£30	£90	£200/£300
Die numbers discontinued.						
1879	1737	Included above	£10	£20	£80	£200/
1880	ND	Hair lock on cheek	£15	£35	£80	£200/£250
1880*	1737C	No lock of hair	£9	£20	£70	£150/
1881	1740	6,239,447	£7	£15	£70	£130/£200
1882	1743	759,809	£12	£30	£100	£200/£300
1883	1744	4,986,558	£7	£18	£60	£120/
1884	1745	3,422,565	£6	£18	£60	£120/
1885	1746	4,652,771	£7	£18	£60	£120/
1886	1748	2,728,249	£7	£18	£60	£120/
1887	1750	3,675,607	£7	£18	£55	£130/

Victoria Young Head 1885 Sixpence

*The Young head Victoria portrait; to the untrained eye looks the same. There were however, minor changes made in 1867, and then again in 1880. The lock of hair on the cheek was removed during 1880 and that accounts for the two types that year.

Jubilee Head 1887 Sixpence.
The withdrawn type

Jubilee Head .925 Fine Silver, 19mm. Weight 3.01g

This first type Jubilee head sixpence was quickly withdrawn due to it being of similar design and roughly the same size as the half sovereign. At least one person was charged for gold plating a sixpence in order to pass it off as a half sovereign.

Reverse A: Gartered Shield, the withdrawn type.

Date	ESC	Mintage	Fine	VF	EF	UNC/BU
1887	1752	3,675,607	£5	£10	£15	£25/£30
1887	1752A	R of Victoria struck over I			£100	£170/
1887	1752B	JEB on truncation	£15	£30	£100	£175/£200
1887	1753	Proof				£70/£100

The B type Sixpences (on the next page) have a wreath reverse, just like that of the previous Young head Sixpence.

VICTORIA Jubilee Head, .925 Fine Silver, 19mm . Weight 3.01g (continued)

Victoria Veiled Head 1893 Sixpence obverse. Reverse type as Edward VII sixpence.

Date	ESC	Mintage	Fine	VF	EF	UNC/BU
Reverse B: Crowned Value in Wreath.						
1887	1754	Included with Rev A	£5	£8	£15	£30/
1888	1756	4,197,698	£5	£8	£25	£50/
1889	1757	8,738,928	£5	£10	£25	£50/
1890	1758	9,386,955	£6	£20	£40	£80/
1891	1759	7,022,734	£6	£20	£40	£80/
1892	1760	6,245,746	£8	£20	£40	£90/
1893*	1761	7,350,619	£400	£600		

* Noted: £225 Fair/Near Fair (R. Ingram Coins 2005)
£130 VG/Near VG (London Coins 2006)

VICTORIA Old or Widow Head, .925 Fine Silver, 19mm. Weight 3.01g

Portrait by Thomas Brock, engraved by George William de Saulles. The reverse was a slightly modified version of the original Jean Baptiste Merlen design.

Date	ESC	Mintage	Fine	VF	EF	UNC/BU
1893	1762	Included above	£5	£8	£20	£35/£50
1894	1764	3,467,704	£6	£10	£28	£50/£65
1895	1765	7,024,631	£5	£10	£24	£45/£60
1896	1766	6,651,699	£5	£10	£24	£35/£45
1897	1767	5,031,498	£5	£10	£24	£35/£45
1898	1768	5,914,100	£5	£10	£24	£40/£60
1899	1769	7,996,804	£5	£10	£24	£40/£60
1900	1770	8,984,354	£8	£10	£30	£40/£60
1901	1771	5,108,757	£5	£9	£20	£30/£50

EDWARD VII .925 Fine Silver, 19mm. Weight 3.01g

From this reign onwards the use of a reducing machine was adopted. The artist is responsible for creating a large version of the design and the old job of creating a smaller version to strike coins is now undertaken mechanically. The engraver being made quite redundant in this respect! George William de Saulles was responsible for the Edward VII portrait and the reverse was a modified version of the previous old head Victoria type.

Edward VII 1906 Sixpence

Date	ESC	Mintage	Fine	VF	EF	UNC/BU
1902	1785	6,367,378	£5	£10	£30	£50/£75
1902	1786	15,123 Proofs with matt finish				£50/£60
1903	1787	5,410,096	£8	£15	£50	£75/£100
1904	1788	4,487,098	£9	£20	£65	£110/£150
1905	1789	4,235,556	£9	£20	£70	£120/£160
1906	1790	7,641,146	£8	£15	£40	£75/£100
1907	1791	8,733,673	£8	£15	£40	£75/£100
1908	1792	6,739,491	£8	£15	£40	£80/£100
1909	1793	6,584,017	£8	£15	£40	£80/£100
1910	1794	12,490,724	£5	£9	£30	£50/£70

GEORGE V .925 Fine Silver (until 1920) 19mm. Weight 3.01g

The bust was by Bertram MacKennal, the reverse was a smaller version of that used for the shilling, which was esentially a modified version of that used for the Edward VII shilling and designed originally by de Saulles.

Date	ESC	Mintage	Fine	VF	EF	UNC/BU
1911	1795	9,155,310	BV	£5	£18	£25/£35
1911	1796	6,007 Proofs				£35/£50
1912	1797	10,984,129	BV	£6	£25	£45/£60
1913	1798	7,499,833	BV	£9	£32	£60/£70
1914	1799	22,714,602	BV	£5	£15	£40/£50
1915	1800	15,694,597	BV	£5	£15	£40/£50
1916	1801	22,207,178	BV	£5	£10	£25/£40
1917	1802	7,725,475	£3	£12	£35	£65/£75
1918	1803	27,558,743	BV	£5	£15	£35/£50
1919	1804	13,375,447	BV	£4	£18	£35/£50
1920	1805	14,136,287. Ag .925	£3	£8	£25	£60/£70

George V 1926 Sixpence. 1st reverse type. Early (1st Effigy) sixpences have a slightly larger bust.

GEORGE V Now debased to .500 Silver, 19mm. Weight 2.876g

Date	ESC	Mintage	Fine	VF	EF	UNC/BU
1920	1806	Silver .500	£2	£4	£15	£30/£45
1921	1807	30,339,741	£2	£4	£15	£25/£35
1922	1808	16,878,890	£2	£4	£20	£20/£30
1923	1809	6,382,793	£2	£4	£20	£35/£50
1924	1810	17,444,218	£2	£4	£20	£35/£45
1925	1811	12,720,558	£2	£5	£16	£40/£50
1925	1812	With new broader rim	£2	£4	£14	£30/£40
1926	1813	21,809,261	£2	£5	£18	£45/£60
1926	1814	Modified Effigy (Ap I)	£2	£5	£10	£35/£50
1927	1815	68,939,873	£2	£4	£10	£35/£45
1927	1816	15,000 Proofs.New Oak/Acorn reverse				£35/£40
1928	1817	23,123,384	BV	£2	£10	£28/£38
1929	1818	28,319,326	BV	£2	£10	£25/£35
1930	1819	16,990,289	BV	£2	£15	£25/£35
1931**	1820	16,873,268	£2	£5	£20	£30/£40
1932	1821	9,406,117	£2	£4	£12	£30/£45
1933	1822	22,185,083	£2	£5	£9	£30/£40
1934	1823	9,304,009	£2	£5	£10	£30/£40
1935	1824	13,995,621	BV	BV	£6	£25/£35
1936	1825	24,380,171	BV	BV	£5	£25/£35

** The later George V Sixpences from 1931 onwards have finer edge millings.

George V 1934 Sixpence. 2nd reverse type

EDWARD VIII .500 Silver 19mm

The reverse featuring six linked rings of St. Edmund designed by George Kruger Gray. The obverse was by Thomas Humphrey Paget. Like all Edward VIII coins, this was not officially issued.

Date	ESC	Mintage	Fine	VF	EF	UNC/BU
1937	1825B	3 or 4 known	Approximately			£30,000

(last known sale was in 1997. An AFDC coin for £12,000)

GEORGE VI .500 Silver (until 1946) 19mm. Weight 2.827g

The obverse portrait of all George VI coins was by Thomas Humphrey Paget. The reverse is by George Kruger Gray. From 1947 the silver content was completely removed and the new coins were made from a copper and nickel alloy (Cupro-Nickel). In 1949 the King gave up his IND:IMP (Emperor of India) title due to that countries new independence. Partly in order to fill the space this left, the reverse was redesigned to use a different monogram.

Date	ESC	Mintage	EF	UNC/BU
1937	1826	22,302,524	BV	£7/£5
1937	1827	26,402 Proofs		£7/£10
1938	1828	13,402,701	BV	£18/£30
1939	1829	28,670,304	BV	£10/£15
1940	1830	20,875,196	BV	£10/£15
1941	1831	23,186,616	BV	£10/£15
1942	1832	44,942,785	BV	£10/£15
1943	1833	46,927,111	BV	£8/£15
1944	1834	37,952,600	BV	£8/£15
1945	1835	39,939,259	BV	£8/£14
1946	1836	43,466,407	BV	£8/£14

George VI 1939 Sixpence.
1st reverse

GEORGE VI Cupro-Nickel (No silver), 19mm. Weight 2.81g

(weights seem to be slightly more for the new monogram type, 1949 - 1952)

Date	ESC	Mintage		EF	UNC/BU
1947	1837	29,993,263		£1	£6/£7
1948	1838	88,323,540		£1	£6/£7
1949*	1838A	41,355,515		£1	£6/£8
1950	1838B	32,741,955		£2	£9/£15
1950	1838C	17,513 Proofs		£2	£10/£15
1951	1838D	40,399,491		£3	£7/£14
1951	1838E	20,000 Proofs		£4	£10/£15
1952	1838F	1,013,477	VF:£10	£30	£80/£150

George VI Sixpence
2nd reverse used from 1949 - 52.

ELIZABETH II Cupro-Nickel (No silver), 19mm . Weight 2.83g

Portrait by Mary Gillick, reverse is by Edgar Fuller, modelled by Cecil Thomas. From 1954 the title BRITT OMN was omitted. All ESC numbers start with 1838, followed by the letter shown.

Date	ESC	Mintage	UNC/BU
1953	H	70,323,876	£1/£2
1953	G	40,000 Proofs	£3/£5
1954*	I	105,241,150	£4/£5
1955	J	109,929,554	£6/£8
1956	K	109,841,555	£4/£5
1957	L	105,654,290	£3/£4
1958	M	123,518,527	£5/£6
1959	N	93,089441	£1/£2
1960	O	103,288,346	£5/£6
1961	P	115,052,017	£5/£6
1962	Q	178,359,637	£2/£3
1963	R	112,964,000	£3/£4
1964	S	152,336,000	£1/£2
1965	T	129,644,000	£1/£2
1966	U	175,696,000	50p/£1
1967	V	240,788,000	30p/£1
1970	W	750,476 Proofs	£3/£4

Elizabeth II 1955 Sixpence

GEORGE III .925 Fine silver, around 23.5mm. Weight 5.65g

The last major issue of shillings for circulation was in 1787. During the latter part of the 18th century captured Spanish colonial silver coins were circulating in Great Britain due to the lack of proper silver coinage. In 1797 the government made this more official by countermarking Spanish colonial coins and making them legal tender for various face values. It wasn't until 1816/17 that a proper re-coinage was undertaken at the new Royal Mint building at Tower Hill, which was fully equipped with the new and proven Boulton/Watt technology (see notes for Cartwheel Twopence). One of the first coins to be struck was the shilling, which interestingly, remained legal tender as 1/20th of a pound sterling until the decimal equivalent (the 5p) was made smaller in 1990. The portrait of George III was the work of Benedetto Pistrucci, as was the reverse. The dies were cut by Thomas Wyon.

Date	ESC	Mintage	Fine	VF	EF	UNC/BU
1816	1228		£15	£30	£70	£120/
1817	1232	23,031,360	£15	£30	£70	£120/
1817	1232A	R over E - GEOE		£150+		
1817	ND	RRIT Error		£60	£150	
1818	1234	1,342,440	£20	£50	£150	£300/
1818	1234A	2nd 8 higher	£30	£60	£165	£300/
1819	1235	7,595,280	£15	£30	£80	£130/
1819	ND	9 over 6			£250	
1819	1235A	9 over 8	£20	£50	£100	£300/
1820	1236	7,975,440	£15	£30	£80	£120/
1820	1236A	I of HONI over S		£60	£150	£300/
1820	ND	H of HONI over sideways H				£500/

George III 1816 Shilling

GEORGE IV .925 Fine Silver, just over 23mm. Weight 5.65g

The first George IV bust was by Benedetto Pistrucci. The obverses and reverses used were the same as the sixpences. The first - used for 1821 only - featured a crowned ornate shield with a large rose under it. The second reverse, used 1823 to 1825, featured a squarer shield with a circular garter surrounding it, and no rose beneath. The third reverse, which is only found with the second obverse (the design by William Wyon) was a complete change and features a lion standing on a large crown.

The first Laureate Head of George IV,
shown with the first and second reverse types.

GEORGE IV .925 Fine silver, around 23.5mm. Weight 5.65g

Date	ESC	Mintage	Fine	VF	EF	UNC/BU
1st Head - Laureate Roman style, 1st Reverse shield.						
1821	1247	2,463,120	£15	£50	£160	£350/
1st Head - Laureate Roman style, 2nd Rev shield.						
1823	1249	693,000	£20	£100	£200	£600/
1824	1251	4,158,000	£15	£50	£150	£350/
1825	1253	2,459,160	£15	£50	£150	£350/
1825	1253B	5 struck over 3	£150			
2nd head - Bare type, 3rd Rev with large lion and crown.						
1825	1254	Inc above	£15	£40	£100	£300/
1825	1254A	Roman I for 1 in date. Fine: £495 (R Ingram 2006)				
1826	1257	6,351,840	£15	£30	£100	£300/
1826	1257A	6/2	£100	£200		
1827	1259	574,200	£35	£100	£300	£500/
1829	1260	879,120	£30	£60	£200	£400/

The second (bare) head and its only reverse (the third George IV shilling reverse)

WILLIAM IV .925 Fine silver, just over 23mm. Weight 5.65g

A larger version of the sixpence, the William IV shilling featured the familar William Wyon bust (from a model by Sir Francis Chantrey) and wreath type reverse by Jean Baptiste Merlen.

Date	ESC	Mintage	Fine	VF	EF	UNC/BU
1834	1268	3,223,440	£18	£40	£180	£350/
1835	1271	1,449,360	£20	£45	£200	£350/
1836	1273	3,567,960	£20	£45	£200	£350/
1837	1276	479,160	£25	£100	£350	
1837	ND	R over low A (noted 2003) "AFDC"				£400/

William IV Shilling obverse.
The reverse used was the wreath type, as with Young Head Victorian Shillings.

VICTORIA .925 Fine silver, around 23.5mm. Weight 5.65g

The Young Head design was the work of William Wyon, the reverse used was basically that used previously for William IV. A few minor changes were made to the bust to age it, although it looked very similar even 50 years into the reign, when it was replaced by the Jubilee bust. Small die numbers were used on the reverse of the dates indicated.

Date	ESC	Mintage	Fine	VF	EF	UNC/BU
1st Young Head						
1838	1278	W.W. 1,956,240	£20	£40	£150	£300/
1839	1280	W.W. 5,666,760	£30	£100	£300	£500/
2nd Young Head (minor differences).						
1839	1283	No W.W. at neck	£20	£40	£150	£300/
1840	1285	1,639,440	£25	£50	£200	£300/
1841	1287	875,160	£30	£50	£200	£400/
1842	1288	2,094,840	£20	£35	£150	£300/
1843	1290	1,465,200	£20	£40	£200	£400/
1844	1291	4,466,880	£20	£35	£150	£300/
1845	1292	4,082,760	£20	£45	£200	£350/
1846	1293	4,031,280	£20	£35	£150	£300/
1848	ND	1,041,480 (More common with 8/6)			£700 EF approx.	
1848	1294	2nd 8 over 6	£60	£150	£500	
1849	1295	645,480	£20	£40	£200	£300/
1850	1296	685,080	£400			
1850	ND	50 over 46		£1000		
1850	1297	50 over 49	£400	£1000		
1851	1298	470,071	£40	£100	£350	
1852	1299	1,306,574	£15	£35	£150	£300/
1853	1300	4,256,188	£15	£35	£100	£220/
1854	1302	552,414	£250	£500		
1854	1302A	4 over 1	£200		£1500	
1855	1303	1,368,499	£15	£30	£150	£280/
1856	1304	3,168,000	£15	£35	£130	£275/
1857	1305	2,562,120	£14	£30	£120	£250/
1857	1305A	Inverted G for D in FD	£125	£400		
1858	1306	3,108,600	£14	£30	£120	£250/
1858	ND	8 over 8		NEF	£200 Approx	
1859	1307	4,561,920	£14	£30	£120	£250/
1859	ND	9 over 8 (or ??) NF: £95 (R Ingram 2006)				
1860	1308	1,671,120	£15	£40	£150	£300/
1861	1309	1,382,040	£15	£40	£150	£300/
1861	ND	1 over tilted 1 Approx			£300	£500/
1862	1310	954,360	£40	£100		
1863	1311	859,320	£50	£100	£350	
1863	1311A	3 over 1		£200	£500	
All shillings (except where stated) now have a small die number above the date until 1879.						
1864	1312	4,518,360	£15	£30	£100	£200/
1865	1313	5,619,240	£15	£30	£100	£200/
1866	1314	4,989,600	£15	£30	£100	£200/
1866	1314A	BBITANNIAR error (Noted: 1995) 'EF' £350				
1867	1315	2,166,120	£15	£30	£100	£250/

Victoria Young head 1839 Shilling

VICTORIA .925 Fine silver, around 23.5mm. Weight 5.65g (continued)

Date	ESC	Mintage	Fine	VF	EF	UNC/BU
3rd Young Head (minor differences).						
1867*	1316		£200	£400		
1868	1318	3,330,360	£12	£30	£100	£220/
1869	1319	736,560	£15	£30	£180	£300/
1870	1320	1,467,471	£15	£30	£150	£300/
1871	1321	4,910,010	£15	£30	£150	£250/
1872	1324	8,897,781	£15	£30	£100	£200/
1872	ND	Raised dot between R and A in GRATIA. NVF: £100				
1873	1325	6,489,598	£10	£25	£100	£200/
1874	1326	5,503,747	£10	£25	£100	£200/
1874	ND	With crosslet 4		£60	£150	£300/
1875	1327	4,353,983	£10	£30	£100	£200/
1876	1328	1,057,487	£15	£40	£120	£250/
1877*	1329	2,980,703	£10	£25	£100	£200/
1878	1330	3,127,131	£20	£60	£120	£250/
1878	As above with die number 1					£400/
1878	ND	Last R in BRITANNIAR over A. Reported 2006.				
1879	1332	3,611,507	£100			
4th Young Head (slightly older features and other minor differences).						
1879	1334	No die no.	£10	£20	£100	£200/
1880	1335	4,842,786	£10	£20	£80	£200/
1881*	1338	5,255,332	£10	£22	£80	£200/
1882	1341	1,611,786	£15	£35	£120	£220/
1883	1342	7,281,4.50	£12	£30	£120	£200/
1884	1343	3,923,993	£10	£20	£100	£180/
1885	1345	3,336,527	£10	£20	£80	£150/
1886	1347	2,086,819	£10	£20	£80	£150/
1887	1349	4,034,133 Young Head	£15	£28	£120	£200/

* 1867 with the third lower relief Young head has not been confirmed to exist. 1877 is also believed to exist without a die number. A variety of 1881 exists with a shorter line under the word SHILLING (ESC 1338A). Both varieties are thought to be equally common.

Victoria Jubilee head 1887 Shilling

VICTORIA Jubilee Head type .925 Fine silver, around 23.5mm . Weight 5.65g

Sir Joseph Boehm designed the Jubilee head, which was engraved by Leonard Charles Wyon. Mr Wyon also engraved the reverse, but from his own design. In 1889 the head was made slightly larger. The old head bust was by Sir Thomas Brock, the reverse of the old head shilling was by Sir Edward Poynter. Both sides of the old head shilling were engraved by George William de Saulles.

Date	ESC	Mintage	Fine	VF	EF	UNC/BU
1887*	1351	Included above	£3	£10	£20	£30/£50
1887	1352	1,312 Proofs				£80/£100
1888	1353	4,526,856 Last 8/7	£8	£10	£25	£90/£160
1889	1354	7,039,628 small head	£30	£100	£275	£400/
1889	1355	Larger head	£8	£11	£30	£100/
1890	1357	8,794,042	£8	£11	£40	£70/£100
1891	1358	5,565,348	£10	£15	£45	£90/
1892	1360	4,591,622	£10	£15	£45	£90/£170

1887 - Varieties with the device that divides the '18' and '87'.

The device pointing to a rim tooth is scarcer than when the device points between two rim teeth.

Old, Veiled or Widow Head type. Weight 5.65g:

Date	ESC	Mintage	Fine	VF	EF	UNC/BU
1893	1361	7,039,074	£6	£12	£30	£120/
1893	1361A	Small letters Obv	£6	£15	£35	£100/
1893	1362	1,312 Proofs				£60/£85
1894	1363	5,953,152	£10	£18	£40	£100/
1895	1364	8,880,651 Small rose	£10	£20	£45	£100/
1895	1364A	Larger rose on Rev	£6	£15	£30	£70/£90
1896	1365	9,264,551 Large rose	£6	£15	£30	£45/£60
1896	1365A	Smaller rose on Rev	£10	£25	£40	£80/£120
1897	1366	6,270,364	£6	£15	£30	£50/£80
1898	1367	9,768,703	£6	£15	£35	£80/£120
1899	1368	10,965,382	£6	£15	£40	£60/£100
1900	1369	10,937,590	£6	£15	£28	£50/£80
1901	1370	3,426,294	£6	£15	£28	£50/£80

Victoria Veiled head 1895 Shilling

EDWARD VII .925 Fine silver, 23.6mm. Weight 5.65g

Both the obverse and reverse were designed and engraved by George William de Saulles.

Date	ESC	Mintage	Fine	VF	EF	UNC/BU
1902	1410	7,809,481	£6	£10	£40	£65/£75
1902	1411	15,123 Proofs with matt finish				£70/£85
1903	1412	2,061,823	£8	£20	£100	£300/
1904	1413	2,040,161	£10	£25	£90	£300/
1905	1414	488,390	£70	£250	£1000	£2000/
1906	1415	10,791,025	£6	£15	£70	£150/
1907	1416	4,083,418	£8	£20	£50	£125/£200
1908	1417	3,806,969	£10	£30	£120	£300/
1909	1418	5,664,982	£15	£75	£150	£300/
1910	1419	26,547,236	£6	£8	£40	£80/£100

Forgeries exist of 1905 shillings.

Edward VII 1910 Shilling

GEORGE V .925 Fine silver (until 1920), 23.6mm. Weight 5.65g

Bust by Sir Bertram MacKennal, reverse as Edward VII type.

Date	ESC	Mintage	Fine	VF	EF	UNC/BU
1911*	1420	20,065,901	BV	£6	£20	£45/£60
1911	1421	6,007 Proofs				£60/£80
1912**	1422	15,594,009	BV	£14	£35	£60/
1913	1423	9,011,509	£6	£15	£50	£100/
1914	1424	23,415,843	BV	£5	£25	£45/£60
1915	1425	39,279,024	BV	£4	£20	£45/£60
1916	1426	35,862,015	BV	£4	£20	£45/£60
1917	1427	22,202,608	BV	£5	£25	£40/£60
1918	1428	34,915,934	BV	£5	£15	£30/£50
1919	1429	10,823,824	£6	£9	£30	£55/£65
Reduced to .500 silver, size and weight as above.						
1920	1430	22,825,142	£3	£10	£25	£45/£60
1921		22,648,763				
	ND	earier, deeper cut bust	£15	£40		
1921	1431	later, shallow larger bust	£3	£15	£35	£70/£100
1922	1432	27,215,738	£3	£4	£25	£40/£50
1923	1433	14,575,243	£3	£4	£12	£30/£50
1924	1434	9,250,095	£3	£6	£18	£35/£40
1925	1435	5,418,764	£3	£12	£50	£100/
1926	1436	22,516,453	£3	£5	£15	£30/£40
1926	1437	Mod Effigy (see Appendix I)	£3	£5	£10	£35/£45
1927	1438	9,262,344	£3	£5	£15	£35/£50

George V 1915 1st type Shilling, 1911-26. The reverse is almost identical to the Edward VII reverse.

1911 exists with the following 3 obverse types:
Obv 1: 'I' of GEORGIUS to space.
Obv 2: 'I' of GEORGIUS to bead and shallow neck.
Obv 3: 'I' of GEORGIUS to bead and fuller neck.

**1912 has been reported with the 'IMP' closely spaced and widely spaced: 'I M P'.

GEORGE V .925 Fine silver (until 1920), 23.6mm. Weight 5.65g
New design with no inner circle and the date to the right. Obverse by MacKennel, reverse by George Kruger Gray.

Date	ESC	Mintage	Fine	VF	EF	UNC/BU
1927	1439	New design		£3	£12	£22/£30
1927	1440	15,000 Proofs				£30/£45
1928	1441	18,136,778		BV	£5	£22/£30
1929	1442	19,343,006		BV	£5	£20/£30
1930	1443	3,137,092	£6	£15	£30	£50/£80
1931	1444	6,993,926		BV	£6	£20/£30
1932	1445	12,168,101		BV	£10	£25/£35
1933	1446	11,511,624		BV	£6	£20/£30
1934	1447	6,138,463		£5	£12	£30/£40
1935	1448	9,183,462		BV	£10	£20/£25
1936	1449	11,910,613		BV	£10	£20/£25

EDWARD VIII, .500 silver, just over 23mm
The reverse was the George VI Scottish type designed by George Kruger Gray. The obverse was by Thomas Humphrey Paget. Like all Edward VIII coins, this was not officially issued.

Date	ESC	Mintage	Fine	VF	EF	UNC/BU
1936	1449B	Pattern Scottish type only			Extremely Rare	

George V 1929 2nd type Shilling. 1927-36

George VI 1942 English type Shilling

GEORGE VI .500 silver (until 1947), just over 23mm. Weight 5.61g
The reverses were by George Kruger Gray. The obverse was by Thomas Humphrey Paget.

Date	ESC	Mintage	EF	UNC/BU
1937E	1450	8,359,122	£3	£9/£12
1937E	1451	Proof 26,402		£8/£10
1937S	1452	6,748,875	£3	£7/£9
1937S	1453	Proof 26,402		£5/£8
1938E	1454	4,833,436	£6	£9/£15
19385	1455	4,797,852	£6	£9/£15
1939E	1456	11,052,677	£6	£10/£12
1939S	1457	10,263,892	£6	£10/£12
1940E	1458	11,099,126	£5	£10/£12
1940S	1459	9,913,089	£4	£9/£11
1941E	1460	11,391,883	£3	£10/£12
1941S	1461	8,086,030	£3	£8/£10
1942E	1462	17,453,643	BV	£10/£12
1942S	1463	13,676,759	BV	£8/£10
1943E	1464	11,404,213	BV	£7/£10
1943S	1465	9,824,214	BV	£7/£10
1944E	1466	11,586,752	BV	£7/£10
1944S	1467	10,990,167	BV	£7/£10
1945E	1468	15,143,404	BV	£7/£8
1945S	1469	15,106,270	BV	£7/£8
1946E	1470	18,663,797 **	BV	£6/£7
1946S	1471	16,381,501	BV	£6/£7
Cupro-Nickel (no silver) Type as before. Weight 5.68g				
1947E	1472	12,120,611	£1	£7/£8
1947S	1473	12,282,223	£1	£7/£8
1948E	1474	45,576,923	£1	£7/£8
1948S	1475	45,351,937	£1	£7/£8
IND : IMP in legend discontinued.				
1949E	1475A	19,328,405	£2	£10/£18
1949S	1475B	21,243,074	£2	£10/£20
1950E	1475C	19,243,872	£5	£10/£20
1950E	1475D	17,513 Proofs	FDC	£20
1950S	1475E	14,299,601	£5	£15/£20
1950S	1475F	17,513 Proofs	FDC	£20
1951E	1475G	9,956,930	£3	£10/£18
1951E	1475H	20,000 Proofs	FDC	£17
1951S	1475I	10,961,174	£3	£10/£18
1951S	1475J	20,000 Proofs	FDC	£15
1952E	1475*	1 known outside of the Royal Collection.		

From 1937 - 1966 (and again for the 1970 proofs) Shillings were struck with either an English or Scottish reverse type. They circulated, generally, throughout the United Kingdom and are indicated in this book by the suffix E or S after the date.

George VI Scottish type Shilling reverse

** 1946E has been reported with two reverse varieties concerning the pointing of the 'IND'.
Reverse A: The 'I' points to a rim bead. Reverse B: The 'I' points between two beads.

Like with a lot of minor varieties on common coins, this is rarely distinguished and the values are assumed to be the same.

ELIZABETH II, Cupro-Nickel (no silver), 23.6mm. Weight 5.63g

The young Elizabeth portrait was designed by Mary Gillick. The English and Scottish reverse types were by William Gardner. As with all the Elizabeth II coins, the BRITT OMN was removed in 1954. All the shillings below have the ESC number 1475 followed by the letter(s) shown.

Date	ESC	Mintage	EF	UNC/BU
1953E	K	41,942,894		£2/£3
1953	ND	Head both sides. Undated but BRITT:OMN present		£300/
1953E	L	Proofs 40,000	FDC	£10
1953S	M	20,663,528		£5/£8
1953S	N	40,000 Proofs	FDC	£8
1954E	O	30,262,032		£5/£7
1954S	P	26,771,735		£7/£9
1955E	Q	45,259,908		£9/£12
1955S	R	27,950,906		£8/£10
		Also exists with broader rim.		
1956E	S	44,907,008		£11/£15
1956S	T	42,853,637		£10/£14
1957E	U	42,774,217		£8/£10
1957S	V	17,959,988		£15/£18
1958E	W	14,392,305		£12/£15
1958S	X	40,822,557		£3/£4
1959E	Y	19,442,778		£4/£8
1959S	Z	1,012,988	£4	£20/£30
1960E	AA	27,027,914		£5/£7
1960S	BB	14,376,932		£5/£7
1961E	CC	39,816,907		£4/£6
1961S	DD	2,762,558	£2	£10/£16
1962E	EE	36,704,379		£4/£6
1962S	FF	18,967,310		£4/£6
1963E	GG	44,714,000		£2/£3
1963S	HH	32,300,000		£2/£3
1964E	II	8,590,900		£2/£3
1964S	JJ	5,239,100		£2/£6
1965E	KK	9,218,000		£1/£2
1965S	LL	2,774,000		£1/£2
1966E	MM	15,005,000 *		£1/£2
1966S	NN	15,607,000 *		£1/£2
1966S		Wrong alignment **		£100/
1970E	OO	Proofs 750,476 from set		£4/
1970S	PP	Proofs 750,476 from set		£4/

* Mintage number includes some struck in 1967, but dated 1966.

** Coin struck with incorrect 'Coin' alignment, see appendix I.

Elizabeth II 1965 Scottish type Shilling

The Elizabeth II English type reverse

Eighteenpence Bank tokens (One Shilling and Sixpence)

This interesting series, issued under the authority of the Bank of England was really an authorised token issue providing much needed change until the major re-coinage of 1816. Two bust types were used on these during their short date run. The first bust is the military type as illustrated, the second bust was a not entirely attractive laureate head type.

GEORGE III .925 Fine Silver, 26mm. Weight, about 7.3g

Date	ESC	Details	F	VF	EF	UNC/BU
1811	969		£15	£28	£75	£200/
1812	971	(1st head)	£15	£28	£80	£200/
1812	972	(2nd head)	£14	£25	£80	£200/
1813	976		£14	£25	£80	£180/
1814	977		£14	£25	£80	£180/
1815	978		£14	£25	£80	£180/
1816	979		£14	£25	£80	£180/

Second head Eighteenpence
Bank Token of 1814

Florins / Two Shillings

VICTORIA .925 fine silver, 28mm. Weight 11.31g. The Godless Florin.

During a time when religion was more widely practised and being a good Christian was a focal point of most peoples lives, it was probably asking for trouble to produce a coin for circulation omitting the words 'DEI GRATIA' (For the grace of god). Even though it was pretty revolutionary, being one tenth of a pound, and therefore Britains first decimal coin, it didn't last long, and was replaced two years later by a redesigned 'Gothic' style florin. William Wyon designed both obverses and William Dyce was responsible for both reverses. Confusingly for novices, the Gothic florins have no numerical date on them, instead; it is in Roman Numerals after the obverse legend.

Date	ESC	Mintage	Roman Date	Fine	VF	EF	UNC/BU
1849	802	413,830		£20	£45	£200	£220/
1849	802A	'WW' initials partly obliterated			£60	£250	£300/
VICTORIA .925 fine silver, 30mm. Weight approx 11.35g. The Gothic Florin.							
1851	803	1,540	mdcccli	£2000+		(reported 1995)	
1852	806	1,014,552	mdccclii	£20	£70	£200	£350/
1852	807A	ii struck over i					£550/
1853	807B	3,919,950	mdcccliii	£15	£60	£200	£400/
1853	808	With no stop after date.		£15	£60	£200	£400/
1854	811	550,413	mdcccliv	£400	£1000		
1855	812	831,017	mdccclv	£20	£60	£200	£400/
1856	813	2,201,760	mdccclvi	£15	£40	£200	£400/
1856	813A	With no stop after date.		£15	£75	£200	£400/
1857	814	1,671,120	mdccclvii	£15	£50	£200	£400/
1858	816	2,239,380	mdccclviii	£18	£50	£200	£350/
1858	816B	With no stop after date.		£18	£40	£200	£400/
1859	817	2,568,060	mdccclvix	£22	£70	£220	£400/£500
1859	818	With no stop after date.		Rare			

Victoria 1849 'Godless' Florin

VICTORIA .925 fine silver, 30mm. Weight approx 11.35g. The Gothic Florin

Date	ESC	Mintage	Roman Date	Fine	VF	EF	UNC/BU
1860	819	1,475,100	mdccclx	£18	£70	£300	£500/
1862	820	594,000	mdccclxii	£100	£500		
1863	822	938,520	mdccclxiii	£1000			
1864	824	1,861,200	mdccclxiv	£20	£75	£300	
1865	826	1,580,044	mdccclxv	£25	£75	£300	
1866	828	914,760	mdccclxvi	£20	£85	£300	
1866	829	With colon after date.		Rare			
1867	830	423,720	mdccclxvii	£20	£65	£300	£500/
1867	832A	No 'WW' (42 arcs in border)			Extremely rare		
1868	833	896,940	mdccclxviii	£15	£50	£200	
1869	834	297,000	mdccclxix	£50	£100	£300	
1870	836	1,080,648	mdccclxx	£50	£100	£300	
1871	837	3,425,605	mdccclxxi	£15	£55	£200	£400/
1872	840	7,199,690	mdccclxxii	£15	£55	£250	£400/
1873	841	5,921,839	mdccclxxiii	£15	£55	£200	£350/
1874	843	1,642,630	mdccclxxiv	£20	£80	£250	£450/
1874	843A	iv struck over iii		£25	£60	(noted	1999)
1875	844	1,117,030	mdccclxxv	£15	£50	£200	£400/
1876	845	580,034	mdccclxxvi	£40	£150		£450/
1877	846	682,292	mdccclxxvii	£15	£50	£200	£400/
1877	847	No 'WW' (48 arcs in border)				£500	
1877	848	No 'WW' (42 arcs in border)			£60	£200	
1878	849	1,786,680	mdccclxxviii	£15	£40	£200	£400/
1879		1,512,247	mdccclxxix :				
	849B	Die No. present, 48 arcs		£30	£75	£200	(with WW)
	850	42 border arcs		£100	£200	(no WW initials)	
	851	No Die No. 48 border arcs		£15	£50	£180	£350/
	852	38 border arcs		£20	£65	£200	
1880	854A	Portrait as 1868-1877. It's difficult to tell the difference between this and the normal 1880 coin below. This type is extremely rare.					
1880	854	2,167,170	mdccclxxx	£20	£50	£200	£400/
1881	856	2,570,337	mdccclxxxi	£20	£60	£200	£400/
1881	858A	Broken die, last 'x' looks like an 'r'				£300	
1883	859	3,555,667	mdccclxxxiii	£15	£50	£190	£350/
1884	860	1,447,379	mdccclxxxiv	£15	£50	£190	£350/
1885	861	1,758,210	mdccclxxxv	£18	£50	£190	£350/
1886	863	591,773	mdccclxxxvi	£15	£45	£190	£350/
1887	865	1,776,903	mdccclxxxvii	£15	£50	£200	£350/
1887	866	'WW' present (46 arcs in border)			£50	£250	£400/

Victoria 1864 'Gothic' Florin

VICTORIA .925 fine silver, Jubilee Head type 29.5mm. Weight approx 11.3g.
Sir Joseph Boehm designed the Jubilee head, which was engraved by Leonard Charles Wyon. Mr Wyon also engraved the reverse, but from his own design. The old head bust was by Sir Thomas Brock, the reverse of the old head florin was by Sir Edward Poynter. Both sides of the old head florin were engraved by George William de Saulles.

Date	ESC	Mintage	Fine	VF	EF	UNC/BU
1887	868	Included with Gothic	£10	£16	£22	£40/£70
1887	869	1,084 Jubilee Head Proofs			£50	£140/£200
1888	870	1,541,540	£10	£20	£60	£120/
1889	871	2,973,561	£10	£20	£60	£120/
1890	872	1,684,737	£12	£45	£100	
1891	873	836,438	£30	£60	£200	£300/
1892	874	283,401	£30	£75	£250	

Victoria Jubilee Head 1887 Florin

VICTORIA .925 fine silver, Veiled or Widow Head 28.5mm. Weight approx 11.3g.

Date	ESC	Mintage	Fine	VF	EF	UNC/BU
1893	876	1,666,103	£9	£20	£50	£100/£130
1894	878	1,952,842	£9	£30	£80	£150/£200
1895	879	2,182,968	£9	£20	£65	£130/£150
1896	880	2,944,416	£9	£20	£65	£130/£150
1897	881	1,699,921	£9	£20	£65	£120/£140
1898	882	3,061,343	£10	£20	£65	£110/£130
1899	883	3,966,953	£10	£20	£65	£100/£120
1900	884	5,528,630	£10	£20	£65	£100/£120
1901	885	2,648,870	£10	£20	£65	£100/£130

EDWARD VII .925 fine silver, 28.5mm. Weight approx 11.3g.
Both the obverse and reverse were designed and engraved by George William de Saulles.

Date	ESC	Mintage	Fine	VF	EF	UNC/BU
1902	919	2,489,575	£15	£25	£70	£85/£120
1902	920	15,123 Matt finish Proofs				£80/£100
1903	921	1,995,298	£20	£50	£200	£400/
1904	922	2,769,932	£20	£55	£200	£500/
1905	923	1,187,596	£50	£200	£600	
1906	924	6,910,128	£15	£30	£200	£400/
1907	925	5,947,895	£15	£30	£200	£400/
1908	926	3,280,010	£20	£70	£300	£800/
1909	927	3,482,289	£22	£90	£200	£550/
1910	928	5,650,713	£10	£25	£150	£300/

Victoria Veiled Head 1893 Florin

Edward VII 1902 Florin

GEORGE V .925 fine silver (until 1919) 28.5mm. Weight approx 11.3g.

The obverse is by Sir Bertram MacKennal (modified at various stages) and the first reverse design, based on the Jubilee Victoria issue is by an unknown designer, probably completed in house. From 1927 onwards the new reverse was designed by George Kruger Gray.

Date	ESC	Mintage	Fine	VF	EF	UNC/BU
1911	929	5,951,284	BV	£15	£35	£80/£100
1911	930	6,007 Proofs			£30	£80/£100
1912	931	8,571,731	BV	£15	£50	£150/
1913	932	4,545,278	£9	£25	£60	£150/
1914*	933	21,252,701	BV	£14	£25	£60/£70
1915	934	12,367,939	BV	£14	£30	£50/£60
1916	935	21,064,337	BV	£14	£30	£50/£60
1917	936	11,181,617	BV	£14	£35	£60/
1918	937	29,211,792	BV	£14	£35	£70/£90
1919	938	9,469,292	BV	£18	£30	£65/£100

George V 1911 Florin

*1914 Large rim teeth or small rim teeth reported.

* 1920 'BRITT' has either 'I' pointing directly at, or between rim beads. Both varieties are rarely distinguished.

GEORGE V .500 silver, 28.5mm

Date	ESC	Mintage	Fine	VF	EF	UNC/BU
1920	ND	Deeper engraved bust	BV	£12	£50	£100/
1920*	939	15,387,833	BV	£9	£30	£65/£80
1921	940	34,863,895	BV	£8	£40	£65/£90
1922	941	23,861,044	BV	£6	£30	£55/£70
1923	942	21,546,533	BV	£6	£25	£50/£60
1923	ND	I of BRITT points to tooth		GVF/NEF: £150		
1924	943	4,582,372	BV	£10	£40	£80/£100
1925	944	1,404,136	£20	£50	£200	£600/
1926	945	5,125,410	BV	£15	£50	£80/£100
1927	947	15,000 Proofs of new design				£65/£80
1928	948	11,087,186	BV	£4	£10	£25/£40
1929	949	16,397,279	BV	£4	£10	£25/£40
1930	950	5,753,568	BV	£8	£20	£40/£50
1931	951	6,556,331	BV	£4	£9	£30/£40
1932	952	717,041	£20	£60	£400	
1933	953	8,685,303	BV	£3	£10	£20/£40
1935	954	7,540,546	BV	£3	£6	£14/£30
1936	955	9,897,448	BV	£3	£5	£14/£25

George V 1936
2nd Type Florin, 1927-36

EDWARD VIII .500 silver, 28.5mm. As George VI but with ER initials.

The planned reverse was the George VI type - with ER instead of GR - designed by George Kruger Gray. The obverse was by Thomas Humphrey Paget. This was not officially issued.

Date	ESC	Mintage	VF	EF	UNC/BU
1937	955A	3-4 Examples known.	Very expensive!		

GEORGE VI .500 silver (until 1946), 28.5mm. Weight 11.33g.

Thomas Humphey Paget designed the bust of George VI. The reverse was the work of George Kruger Gray.

Date	ESC	Mintage	VF	EF	UNC/BU
1937	956	13,006,781	BV	£3	£8/£12
1937	957	26,402 Proofs			£12/£20
1938	958	7,909,388	£3	£7	£25/£30
1939	959	20,850,607	BV	£4	£6/£10
1940	960	18,700,338	BV	£3	£10/£15
1941	961	24,451,079	BV	£3	£9/£15
1942	962	39,895,243	BV	£3	£5/£10
1943	963	26,711,987	BV	£3	£6/£10
1944	964	27,560,005	BV	£3	£5/£10
1945	965	25,858,049	BV	£3	£5/£10
1946	966	22,910,085	BV	£3	£5/£10
Now Cupro-Nickel (no silver), 28.5mm. Weight 11.3g.					
1947	967	22,910,085		£1	£5/£10
1948	968	67,553,636		£1	£5/£10
1949	968A	28,614,939		£1	£10/£20
1950	968B	24,357,490		£2	£10/£20
1950	968C	17,513 Proofs		FDC	£20
1951	968D	27,411,747		£3	£10/£20
1951	968E	20,000 Proofs		FDC	£20

George VI 1937 Florin.
IND:IMP was removed in 1949.

ELIZABETH II Cupro-Nickel (no silver), 28.5mm. Weight 11.5g

The bust was by Mary Gillick, the reverse was the work of Edgar Fuller, modelled by Cecil Thomas. As with the other denominations, the 1953 coins usually have poorly defined details on the head. The dies were improved for the 1954 issue onwards. In 1954 the title BRITT OMN was removed from the coins.

Date	ESC	Mintage	EF	UNC/BU
1953	968F	11,958,710	£1	£2/£4
1953	968G	40,000 Proofs		£10/£12
1954	968H	13,085,422	£10	£25/£35
1955	968I	25,887,253	£2	£5/£8
1956	968J	47,824,500	£2	£5/£8
1957	968K	33,071,282	£8	£25/£30
1958	968L	9,564,580	£5	£12/£20
1959	968M	14,080,319	£6	£15/£25
1960	968N	13,831,782	£1	£4/£6
1961	968O	37,735,315	£1	£4/£6
1962	968P	35,147,903	50p	£3/£5
1963	968Q	25,562,000	50p	£3/£5
1964	968R	16,539,000	50p	£2/£5
1965	968S	48,163,000	50p	£1/£3
1966	968T	84,041,000	50p	£1/£2
1967*	968U	39,718,000	50p	£1/£2
1967	ND	Double tails error	£100	
1970	968V	Proofs 750,476 from set		£3/£4

*1967 Mintage figure includes over 17 million struck in 1968 but dated 1967

Eliabeth II 1965 Florin. The 1953 Florins had BRITT:OMN in the obverse legend.

GEORGE III .925 fine silver, 32mm. Weight 14.1g

The last Half Crowns issued for circulation before 1817 were dated 1751 (George II), although Spanish coins were countermarked with the bust of George III to supply the demand until the re-coinage of 1816. Thomas Wyon junior (cousin of William Wyon) was responsible for the first head, which became known as the 'Bull' head. The King didn't like it, and it was changed in 1817 to a Pistrucci version. Thomas Wyon designed the first half crown reverse, and the second was a modified version.

Date	ESC	Mintage	Fine	VF	EF	UNC/BU
1st 'Bull' style head						
1816	613		£35	£100	£300	£550/
1817	616	8,092,656	£30	£80	£250	£500/
1817	616A	'D' of 'DEI' over 'T'	£50	£200		
1817	ND	E of DEF over R&E		£400		
1817	ND	S of PENSE over I		£200		
2nd Type, with Re-designed smaller head and new reverse.						
1817	618	Included above	£35	£85	£300	£500/
1817	618A	S's in Motto mirrored			Very Rare	
1818	621	2,905,056	£35	£100	£300	£500/
1819	623	4,790,016	£30	£90	£250	£500/
1819	ND	9 Struck over 8		£900	Adams/Spink 2005	
1819	ND	HO & SO over smaller ho & so		£240	Adams/Spink 2005	
1820	625	2,396,592 (Inc GIV)	£40	£100	£300	£500/

George III 1817 1st type
'Bull Head' Half Crown

George III 1818 2nd Type Half Crown

GEORGE IV .925 fine silver, 32mm. Weight 14.1g

Bennedetto Pistrucci designed the first Romanesque laureate head but refused to copy Sir Francis Chantrey's work, so the second bust was engraved by William Wyon. All three reverses were the work of Jean Baptiste Merlen. The first and second reverse types are very similar to the respective shilling reverses. The third reverse is illustrated below.

Date	ESC	Mintage	Fine	VF	EF	UNC/BU
1st Roman style Laureate head.						
1820	628	Inc above, 1st Rev	£20	£70	£250	£500/
1821	631	1,435,104, 1st Rev	£30	£70	£250	£500/
1821*	ND	Heavier garnishing 1st Rev	£50	£120	£400	
1823	633	2,003,760 1st Rev	£500	£2000		
1823	634	Inc above, 2nd Rev	£30	£80	£300	£500/
1824	636	465,696 ?	£40	£90	£350	£600/
2nd Bare, thinner William Wyon head with 3rd reverse.						
1824	639	3-4 known, 3rd Rev	Very expensive!			
1825	642	2,258,784	£35	£80	£250	£500/
1826	646	2,189,088	£35	£80	£250	£500/
1828	648	49,890 ?	£70	£200	£600	
1829	649	508,464	£60	£100	£400	

George IV 1st head

* 1821 - The reverse type with heavier shield garnishing also has the left leg of the A of ANNO pointing just to the right of a rim denticle. has heavier shield garnishing.

George IV 1825 Half Crown (2nd head)

William IV 1834 Half Crown

WILLIAM IV .925 fine silver, 32mm. Weight 14.1g

Jean Baptiste Merlen designed and engraved the reverse

Date	ESC	Mintage	Fine	VF	EF	UNC/BU
1831	656	5-10 examples	Very expensive!			
1834	660	993,168 block WW	£40	£200	£600	£1000/
1834	662	WW script	£15	£60	£180	£500/
1835	665	281,952	£35	£100	£400	
1836	666	1,588,752	£30	£80	£200	£500/
1836	666A	6 over 5	£30	£100	£500	£1000/
1837	667	150,526	£80	£150	£500	£800/

VICTORIA .925 fine silver, 32mm. Weight 14.1g

W Wyon designed and engraved the young head of Queen Victoria. In 1874 the design was modified and struck in lower relief. J B Merlen designed and engraved the reverse.

Date	ESC	Mintage	Fine	VF	EF	UNC/BU
Young Head:						
1839	672	WW incuse	£600	£2000		
1840	673	386,496	£90	£250	£550	
1841	674	42,768	£700	£1500	£3400	
1842	675	486,288	£40	£100	£600	
1843	676	454,608	£100	£300	£1000	£2000/
1844	677	1,999,008	£50	£150	£600	£1000/
1845	679	2,231,856	£40	£100	£500	£1000/
1846	680	1,539,668	£60	£150	£600	£1000/
1846	ND	8 over 6	£500	Adams/Spink 2005		
1848	681	Irregular obv lettering			£1300	
1848*	681A	367,488. 8/6			£1400	
1848	ND	8 over 7	£400			
1849	682	261,360 large date		£150	£500	
1849	683	Small date	£100	£250	£900	
1849	ND	9 over 7 (or double struck 9) Fine: £200				
1850	684	484,613		£150	£350	£500/
1874	692	2,188,599	£30	£90	£220	£350/
1875	696	1,113,483	£40	£70	£250	£350/
1876	699	633,221	£30	£50	£220	£350/
1876	699A	6 over 5	£30	£50	£180	£350/
1877	700	447,059	£25	£40	£180	£350/
1878	701	1,466,232	£25	£50	£180	£350/
1879	703	901,356	£30	£100	£300	£500/
1880	705	1,346,350	£30	£60	£180	£300/
1881	707	2,301,495	£25	£60	£250	£320/
1882	710	808,227	£30	£100	£250	£450/
1883	711	2,982,779	£20	£65	£200	£300/
1884	712	1,569,175	£20	£65	£200	£300/
1885	713	1,628,438	£20	£65	£200	£300/
1886	715	891,767	£20	£65	£200	£300/
1887	717	261,747	£35	£140	£250	£350/

1839 - A: Queen has one plain, and one ornamented hair tie. B: Queen has two ornamental hair ties.

Victoria Young Head 1874 Half Crown

VICTORIA Jubilee head .925 fine silver, 32mm. Weight 14.1g

Sir Joseph Boehm designed the Jubilee head, which was engraved by Leonard Charles Wyon. Mr Wyon also engraved the reverse, from his own design. The old head bust was by Sir Thomas Brock, who was also responsible for the reverse design. Both sides of the old head half crown were engraved by George William de Saulles.

Date	ESC	Mintage	Fine	VF	EF	UNC/BU
1887	719	1,176,299	£10	£20	£25	£50/£70
1887	720	1,084 Proofs				£150/£175
1888	721	1,428,787	£10	£20	£60	£130/
1889	722	4,811,954	£10	£20	£60	£130/
1890	723	3,228,111	£10	£20	£70	£150/
1891	724	2,284,632	£12	£25	£80	£150/
1892	725	1,710,946	£14	£20	£90	£170/
Old, Veiled, or Widow Head type:						
1893	726	1,792,600	£10	£20	£40	£90/£120
1893	727	1,312 Proofs				£200/
1894	728	1,524,960	£12	£20	£100	£200/
1895	729	1,772,662	£16	£30	£80	£200/£250
1896	730	2,148,505	£14	£20	£60	£150/£200
1897	731	1,678,643	£14	£20	£70	£150/£200
1898	732	1,870,055	£14	£20	£50	£100/£150
1899	733	2,863,872	£14	£20	£50	£100/
1900	734	4,479,128	£14	£25	£60	£120/
1901	735	1,516,570	£14	£20	£50	£120/£200

Victoria Jubilee Head 1887 Half Crown

Victoria Veiled Head 1893 Half Crown

EDWARD VII .925 fine silver, 32mm. Weight 14.14g

Both obverse and reverse were the work of George William de Saulles.

Date	ESC	Mintage	Fine	VF	EF	UNC/BU
1902	746	1,316,008	£20	£35	£75	£120/£150
1902	747	15,123 Matt Proofs			£70	£150/
1903	748	274,840	£150	£500	£2200	
1904	749	709,652	£70	£200	£500	£1200/
1905	750	166,008	£450	£1600	£10,000/	
1906	751	2,886,206	£35	£50	£250	£450/
1907	752	3,693,930	£20	£50	£200	£400/
1908	753	1,758,889	£30	£90	£500	
1909	754	3,051,592	£20	£50	£350	£600/£750
1910	755	2,557,685	£20	£40	£200	£400/

GEORGE V .925 fine silver (until 1920), 32mm. Weight 14.14g

The obverse is by Sir Bertram MacKennal (which was modified at various stages) and the first reverse design is a slightly modified version of the Edward VII type. From 1927 onwards a different reverse was used, this was designed by George Kruger Gray.

Date	ESC	Mintage	Fine	VF	EF	UNC/BU
1911	757	2,914,573	BV	£20	£50	£150/
1911	758	6,007 Proofs				£100/£150
1912	759	4,700,789	BV	£20	£60	£200/
1913	760	1,090,160	£12	£25	£60	£200/
1914	761	18,333,003	BV	£14	£30	£80/£100
1915	762	32,433,066	BV	£10	£30	£80/£100
1916	763	29,530.020	BV	£10	£35	£80/
1917	764	11,172.052	BV	£10	£35	£80/£100
1918	765	29,079,592	BV	£10	£35	£80/£100
1919	766	10,266,737	BV	£10	£35	£80/£100

Edward VII 1909 Half Crown

George V 1917 Half Crown

GEORGE V Debased .500 silver, 32mm. Weight 14.14g:

Date	ESC	Mintage	Fine	VF	EF	UNC/BU
1920	767	17,983,077	BV	£10	£40	£80/£100
1920	ND	Small head, high relief Obv 1/Rev B (2001) BU £110				
1921	768	23,677,889	BV	£10	£25	£80/£100
1922*	769	16,396,774 Rev A	BV	£10	£30	£80/£100
	ND	Rev B	BV	£10	£25	£90/£120
1923	770	26,308,526	BV	£10	£25	£50/£70
1924	771	5,866,294	BV	£8	£40	£70/£95
1925	772	1,413,461	£20	£70	£300	£600/
1926	773	4,473,516	BV	£30	£80	£180/
1926	773A	No colon after OMN	£10	£30	£165	£260/
1926	774	Mod Effigy (Appendix I)	BV	£20	£35	£100/
1927	775	6,852,872	BV	£10	£30	£70/
1927	776	15,000 Proofs of New design				£60/£70
1928*	777	18,762,727	BV	£8	£15	£45/£60
1929*	778	17,632,636	BV	£8	£15	£35/£50
1930	779	809,501	£20	£80	£250	
1931	780	11,264,468	BV	£5	£15	£40/£50
1932	781	4,793,643	BV	£7	£15	£30/£50
1933	782	10,311,494	BV	£7	£10	£20/£30
1934	783	2,422,399	BV	£8	£30	£70/£90
1935	784	7,022,216	BV	£7	£15	£30/£40
1936	785	7,039,423	BV	£7	£9	£25/£40
1936	ND	Prooflike/Early strike				£70/

George V 1935 Half Crown reverse.
Used 1927-1936

EDWARD VIII, .500 silver, 32mm

The proposed reverse by George Kruger Gray featured a rectangular Royal standard flag. The obverse was by Thomas Humphrey Paget. This coin was never officially issued, and the reverse was not used again.

Date	ESC	Mintage	Fine	VF	EF	UNC/BU
1937	785A	Royal arms Flag reverse. Approx				£30,000+

George VI 1945 Half Crown

GEORGE VI .500 silver (until 1946), 32mm. Weight 14.14g
Thomas Humphey Paget designed the bust of George VI. The reverse was the work of George Kruger Gray.

Date	ESC	Mintage	EF	UNC/BU
1937	786	9,106,440	BV	£12/£20
1937	787	26,402 Proofs	FDC	£25
1938	788	6,426,478	£10	£25/£35
1939	789	15,478,635	BV	£15/£20
1940	790	17,948,439	BV	£8/£10
1941	791	15,773,984	BV	£8/£10
1942	792	31,220,090	BV	£8/£10
1942	ND	Specimen strike (also of 1943)		£80/
1943	793	15.462,875	BV	£9/£12
1944	794	15,255,165	BV	£9/£12
1945	795	19,849,242	BV	£5/£8
1946	796	22,724,873	BV	£5/£8
Cupro-Nickel (No Silver), 32mm. Weight 14.22g:				
1947	797	21,911,484	£2	£5/£7
1948	798	71,164,703	£2	£4/£6
IND: IMP legend (Emperor of India) discontinued.				
1949	798A	28,272,512	£3	£10/£15
1950	798B	28,335,500	£5	£15/£20
1950	798C	17,513 Proofs	FDC	£25
1951	798D	9,003,520	£5	£25/
1951	798E	20,000 Proofs	FDC	£25
1952	798F	1 or 2 Known	Approx	£30,000

ELIZABETH II Cupro-Nickel (No Silver), 32mm. Weight 14.2g
Mary Gillick designed the first bust of Elizabeth II. The reverse was the work of Edgar Fuller, modeled by Cecil Thomas.

Date	ESC	Mintage	EF	UNC/BU
1953	798G	4,333,214	£1	£3/£5
1953	798H	40,000 Proofs	FDC	£20
1954	798I	11,614,953	£10	£40/£50
1955	798J	23,628,726	£1	£9/£13
1956	798K	33,934,909	£2	£14/£25
1957	798L	34,200,563	£2	£7/£9
1958	798M	15,745,668	£3	£22/£30
1959	798N	9,028,844	£4	£15/£25
1960	798O	19,929,191		£7/£10
1961	798P	25,887,89		£3/£5
1962	798S	24,013,312		£2/£4
1963	798T	17,557,600		£2/£4
1964	798U	5,973,600		£2/£4
1965	798V	9,878,400		£1/£3
1966	798W	13,384,000		£1/£2
1967	798X	33,058,400		60p/£1
1970	798Y	Proofs from the set		£6/£10

Elizabeth II 1966 Half Crown

Bank of England Tokens

GEORGE III .925 fine silver, 34-35mm. Accurate weight not known at time of writing.
Another short token issue, struck under the authority of the Bank of England in order to provide much needed change until the major re-coinage of 1816. Two bust types were used on these during their short run. The first bust is the military type as shown below, the second bust was a not entirely attractive laureate head type. There are five non proof varieties of 1811, and six different proof types! The die varieties can be identified using: on the obverse, the front leaf of the laurel and its relationship with the 'E' of 'DEI', and on the reverse, the number of acorns in the oak wreath:

Type 1 = Obv: front leaf points to end of 'E'. Rev: has 27 acorns present.
Type 2 = Obv: front leaf points to end of 'E'. Rev: has 26 acorns present.
Type 3 = Obv: front leaf points to gap between 'D' and 'E'. Rev: has 26 acorns present.
Type 4 = Obv: front leaf points to gap between 'D' and 'E'. Rev: has 25 acorns present.
Type 5 = Obv: front leaf points to the upright of 'E'. Rev: has 24 acorns present.

Date	ESC	Mintage or Details	Fine	VF	EF	UNC/BU
1811	407	Type 1(Scarce)	£20	£60	£200	
1811	408	Type 2(Commonest)	£20	£60	£150	
1811	410	Type 3(Rarer)	£20	£70	£150	
1811	411	Type 4(Rarer)	£20	£70	£150	
1811	413	Type 5(Rarer)	£20	£70	£150	
1812	415	(1st head)	£20	£70	£150	£200/
1812	416	(2nd head)	£20	£70	£170	£200/
1813	421		£20	£70	£150	
1814	422		£20	£70	£150	
1815	423		£20	£70	£150	
1816	424		£200	£500		

George III Three Shilling Bank Token. On the obverse, the front leaf of the laurel points to the gap between the 'D' and 'E'.

VICTORIA .925 fine silver, 36mm. Weight 22.62g

Sir Joseph Boehm designed the Jubilee head, which was engraved by Leonard Charles Wyon. Mr Wyon also engraved the reverse, from his own design. The denomination was not popular, as it was often confused for a crown and became known as the 'barmaids ruin'.

Date	ESC	Mintage or Details	Fine	VF	EF	UNC/BU
1887	394	483,347 Roman I	£20	£30	£65	£120/
1887	395	Arabic 1 in date	£20	£30	£60	£100/
1888	397	243,340	£25	£40	£90	£140/
1888*	397A	Inverted 1 VICTORIA	£25	£45	£150	£450/
1889	398	1,185,111	£20	£25	£100	£150/
1889*	398A	Inverted 1 VICTORA	£25	£45	£150	£450/
1890	399	782,146	£20	£40	£100	£150/

* The second 'I' in 'VICTORIA' appears to be an upside-down digit '1'. It is in fact a damaged letter 'I'.

Queen Victoria Jubilee Head 1887
Double Florin with Arabic '1'.

There are also 2 slightly different obverse types noted for the 'Arabic' 1887 coin. The easiest way to spot them concerns the 'D' of 'DEI' and exactly to which bead in the Crown it is level with. Both types are believed common.

Bank of England Five Shilling token

GEORGE III .925 fine silver, 41mm. Accurate weight not known at time of writing.
The largest denomination of the Bank of England token issues. The Dollar started life with a face value of five shillings, but did rise to five shillings and sixpence for six years while silver was in short supply. All are dated 1804, although they were struck up to 1811 and remained legal tender until 1820, by which time their face value was back to five shillings. There are seventeen proof varieties of this coin in various metals, and ten non proof varieties, as a result of slightly different obverse and reverse die combinations being used. They were struck on Spanish/Spanish colonial Pieces of Eight and coins with lots of Spanish detail, especially dates and mintmarks do attract a premium. A picture of an 1804 Dollar can be seen on the previous page.

Type 1 = Obv: front leaf points to upright of 'E'. Rev: raised 'K' under shield.
Type 2 = Obv: front leaf points to upright of 'E'. Rev: inverted incuse 'ꓘ'.
Type 3 = Obv: as above, but no stops between CHK on neck. Rev: raised 'K' under shield.
Type 4 = Obv: as 1 but leaf points to centre of 'E'. Rev: raised 'K' under shield.
Type 5 = Obv: as 1 but leaf points to centre of 'E'. Rev: inverted raised 'ꓘ'
Type 6 = Obv: as 1 but leaf points to centre of 'E'. Rev: inverted incuse 'ꓘ'.
Type 7 = Obv: as 1 but leaf points to right end of 'E'. Rev: raised 'K' under shield.
Type 8 = Obv: as 1 but leaf points to right end of 'E'. Rev: inverted raised 'ꓘ'
Type 9 = Obv: as 1 but leaf points to right end of 'E'. Rev: inverted incuse 'ꓘ'.
Type 10 = Obv: no stop after REX, leaf to centre of 'E'. Rev: raised 'K' under shield.

Date	ESC	Type	Fine	VF	EF
1804	144	Type 1 (commonest)	£140	£300	£500
1804	147	Type 2 (very rare)	£190	£350	
1804	148	Type 3 (rare)	£150	£350	£550
1804	149	Type 4 (scarce)	£150	£350	
1804	153	Type 5 (rare)	£180	£300	
1804	156	Type 6 (scarce)	£180	£350	
1804	158	Type 7 (ext. rare)	£250	£500	
1804	159	Type 8 (very rare)	£190	£350	
1804	162	Type 9 (very rare)	£180	£350	
1804	164	Type 10 (common)	£150	£300	

George III Dollar Bank Token. On the obverse, the front leaf points to the upright of the 'E'.

GEORGE III .925 fine silver, 37.6mm. Weight 28.2759g

Dies designed and engraved by Benedetto Pistrucci. This was the first time a St George and the Dragon design had been used since the reign of Henry VIII.

Date	Edge	ESC	Mintage	Fine	VF	EF	UNC/BU
1818	LVIII	211	155,232	£40	£100	£300	£500/£600
1818*	LVIII	213A	Error edge	£1000	£1800	£3750	
1818	LIX	214	Inc above	£40	£100	£300	£500/£600
1819	LIX	215	683,496	£40	£100	£300	£500/£600
1819	LIX	215A	No stops on edge	£50	£150	£400	
1819	LIX	215B	9 over 8	£100	£200	£500	
1819	LX	216	Inc above	£40	£100	£400	£600/£700
1819*	LX	ND	TVTAMEN	£70	£150	£400	
1820	LX	219	448,272	£50	£100	£500	£700/£900
1820	LX	220A	20 over 19		£200	£600	
1820	LX	ND	S over T (Soit)		£150	£500	

* 1818 Error edge reads: DECVS ANNO REGNI ET TVTAMEN.
* 1819 No stop after the word TVTAMEN.

George III 1818 Crown

George IV 1821 Crown

GEORGE IV .925 fine silver, Laureate Roman style head 37.6mm. Weight 28.2759g
The obverse and reverse were designed by Benedetto Pistrucci and engraved by Jean Baptiste Merlen.

Date	Edge	ESC	Mintage	Fine	VF	EF	UNC/BU
1821	SEC*	246	437,976	£50	£200	£600	£1500/
1822	SEC*	251	124,929	£50	£250	£700	£1500/
1822	TER*	252	Inc Above	£50	£200	£600	£1500/

* SEC = SECUNDO, TER= TERTIO - Regnal year on the edge.

WILLIAM IV .925 fine silver, 38mm. No William IV Crowns were issued for general circulation.

VICTORIA .925 fine silver Young Head, 38mm. Weight approx 28.35g
William Wyon produced the Young head Victoria portrait. The reverse was the work of Jean Baptiste Merlen, before his retirement in 1844.

Date	Edge	ESC	Mintage	Fine	VF	EF	UNC/BU
1844	VIII	280	94,248 Star stops	£50	£200	£1000	
1844	VIII	281	Cinquefoil stops*	£50	£300	£1500	
1845	VIII	282A	159,192 Star stops	£50	£200	£1000	£2500/
1845	VIII	ND	Star stops, error edge, reads: AANNO			£2000	
1845	VIII	282	Cinquefoil stops*	£50	£200	£1000	£2500/
1847	XI	286	140,976	£100	£500	£1400	£2500/
1847**	UNDECIMO		ESC 288*, 8,000 All Proofs		£800	£1500	£3000/

* A cinquefoil is a pattern of five leaves.
** The Gothic Crown as featured on front cover. See also last page.

Above: Victoria Young Head 1845 Crown.

VICTORIA .925 fine silver Jubilee Head, 38.6mm.. Weight approx 28.35g

Sir Joseph Boehm designed the Jubilee head, which was engraved by Leonard Charles Wyon. The reverse on both the jubilee head crown and the old head crown is the classic Benedetto Pistrucci St George slaying the dragon design. The old head bust was by Sir Thomas Brock. A regnal edge year was used on the old head crown, and because Victoria was not crowned on January 1st, this results in two different regnal year types for each date.

Date	ESC	Mintage	Fine	VF	EF	UNC/BU
1887	296	173,581	£25	£35	£80	£150/
1887	297	1,084 Proofs			£300	£600/
1888	298	131,899 Close date	£25	£35	£100	£250/
1888	ND	Wide date	£90	£200	£500	
1889	299	1,807,223	£25	£35	£80	£200/
1890	300	997,862	£25	£38	£100	£200/
1891	301	566,394	£25	£38	£100	£250/
1892	302	451,334	£30	£45	£150	£300/

Victoria 1887 Jubilee Head Crown

VICTORIA .925 fine silver Old, Veiled or Widow Head, 38.6mm.. Weight approx 28.35g

Date	Edge	ESC	Mintage	Fine	VF	EF	UNC/BU
1893	LVI	303	497,845	£25	£35	£150	£300/
1893	LVI	304	1,312 Proofs			£150	£300/
1893	LVII	305	Inc Above	£30	£70	£200	£300/
1894	LVII	306	144,906	£25	£50	£150	£300/
1894	LVIII	307	Inc Above	£25	£50	£150	£300/
1895	LVII	308	252,862	£25	£50	£150	£300/
1895	LIX	309	Inc Above	£25	£60	£150	£300/
1896	LIX	310	317,599	£25	£50	£150	£300/
1896	LX	311	Inc Above	£25	£50	£150	£300/
1897	LX	312	262,118	£25	£50	£150	£300/
1897	LXI	313	Inc Above	£25	£50	£150	£300/
1898	LXI	314	161,450	£35	£100	£300	£600/
1898	LXII	315	Inc Above	£25	£40	£150	£300/
1899	LXII	316	166,300	£25	£40	£150	£300/
1899	LXIII	317	Inc Above	£25	£40	£150	£320/
1900	LXIII	318	353,356	£25	£55	£200	£350/
1900	LXIV	319	Inc Above	£25	£60	£200	£350/

Queen Victoria Veiled Head 1893 Crown

Edward VII 1902 Crown. (Reverse type was the same as the Veiled Head Victorian crowns)

EDWARD VII .925 fine silver, 38.6mm.. Weight approx 28.35g

A one year only issue, and the very last British crown made for circulation (the latter ones being commemorative/ special issues only). The bust is by George William de Saulles, and the reverse is the St George type by Benedetto Pistrucci.

Date	Edge	ESC	Mintage	Fine	VF	EF	UNC/BU
1902	II	361	256,020	£50	£100	£200	£300/
1902	II	362	15,123 Matt Proofs			£150	£250/

GEORGE V .500 silver, 38.6mm. Weight approx 28.4g

In 1927 the mint decided to produce proof sets of the newly designed coinage. The crown, among other coins, was produced as a proof striking only, to be sold in these sets. The design was popular, so subsequently a small number of crowns were struck annually, mainly to provide the public with keepsakes, which were often given as gifts at Christmas time. The popular 'Wreath' crown was produced annually (except 1935) until the death of the king in 1936. In 1935 to celebrate the king's Silver Jubilee a larger number of special crowns were struck featuring an Art Deco St George slaying the dragon. The bust on both coins was the standard Bertram MacKennal design. The wreath reverse was by George Kruger Gray, and the jubilee crown reverse was by Percy Metcalfe. Many have criticized the Art Deco St George, but personally I think it looks classically 1930s, and makes a nice change from the Pistrucci version. The king himself had mixed feelings, saying that St George looked 'A damned bad rider'. The design was approved, so he couldn't have entirely hated it!

Date	Edge	ESC	Mintage	Fine	VF	EF	UNC/BU
1927		367	15,030 Proofs			£150	£250/£350
1928		368	9,034	£100	£150	£300	£400/
1929		369	4,994	£100	£150	£300	£400/
1930		370	4,847	£120	£160	£350	£450/
1931		371	4,056	£100	£160	£320	£400/
1932		372	2,395	£200	£400	£550	£800/
1933		373	7,132	£100	£160	£300	£450/
1934		374	932	£1500	£2000	£3000	£4000/£5000
1935*		375	714,769 incuse edge		£10	£20	£30/
1935*		375A	Error edge lettering**		£900		
1935*		376	SPECIMEN striking, in original box				£50/£60
1936		381	2,473	£200	£300	£500	£700/

* The 1935 coins all feature the George slaying the dragon reverse, not the wreath type reverse.
**The non proof 1935 error edge has a large space after 'ANNO' and some missing letters.

Left to right - The first two images are the obverse and reverse of a 1928 Wreath Crown. The last image is the reverse of the 1935 Crown. The 1935 Crown obverse was similar to the Wreath Crown.

EDWARD VIII .500 silver, 38.6mm

Date	ESC	Mintage	VF	EF	UNC/BU
1937	391C	Reverse as George VI 1937. Approximately			£75,000

GEORGE VI .500 silver, 38.6mm . Weight approx 28.2g

The bust for all George VI coins was by Thomas Humphrey Paget. The reverse of the coronation coin was by George Kruger Gray. The reverse of the 1951 Festival of Britain coin was created by re-using an 1899 crown die with a manually adjusted date. The Festival of Britain crown boxes exist as either matchbox/slide open style, or as boxes with a lift off lid. Coins in green boxes are a little less common.

Date	ESC	Mintage	VF	EF	UNC/BU
1937	392	418,699 Coronation	£10	£20	£30/£40
1937	393	26,402 Proofs from the sets			£40/£50

Cupro-Nickel (No silver), 38.6mm. Struck for the Festival of Britain in 1951.

Date	ESC	Mintage	VF	EF	UNC/BU
1951	393C	1,983,540 Highly prooflike		£5	£7/£10
1951		In box of issue, green or purple		£6	£10/£18
1951	ND	Error edge lettering - Blundered latin date and large space			
		before 'FLORET' (Predecimal.com 2006)			£300/
1951	ND	Error edge lettering - partial overlapping			£200/

The reverse of the 1937 Crown (obv is similar to the 1951 Crown, but with 'FIVE SHILLINGS' under the bust).

1951 Crown - The reverse used for these was a re-cycled 1899 Crown die with the date amended by hand

Queen Elizabeth II 1953 Crown

ELIZABETH II Cupro-Nickel (No silver), 38.6mm . Weight 28.2g (28.4g 1965)

The coronation crown was an interesting departure from tradition, featuring the monarch on horseback; the first time this had been done since the reign of Charles I. Gilbert Ledward designed the obverse and the reverse was a joint effort by Edgar Fuller and Cecil Thomas. The edge has the words 'FAITH AND TRUTH I WILL BEAR UNTO YOU'. The New York Trades fair and Churchill crowns have the young bust by Mary Gillick. The Trades Fair crown uses the same reverse as the coronation crown. The reverse of the Churchill crown was modelled from a bust by Croatian artist Oscar Nemon. The actual bust, which is now part of the Government Art Collection looks much nicer than the quite low relief design on the much criticized crown.

Date	ESC	Mintage	VF	EF	UNC/BU
1953	393F	5,962,621		£3	£4/£6
1953	393G	40,000 Proofs		£15	£20/£30
1953	ND	(Hip Hop) Edge Error: "...WILL BEAR UNTO YO" (no 'U')			
			£30	£40	£60/£80
1960	393K	1,024,038 British Trades Fair issue		£4	£8/
1960	393L	70,000 Polished die specials in box		£7	£15/£20
1965	393N	19,640,000 Churchill issue		25p	75p/£1

From left to right: The obverse of the 1960 Crown (Reverse type was as the 1953 Crown). Obv and Rev of the 1965 Churchill Crown.

Guinea based denominations 1797 - 1815

Introduced in 1663 to coincide with a full range of new milled coins that replaced their hammered (hand struck) predecessors, the guinea and it's fractions and multiples circulated until 1815. Most of the early guineas were made of gold from Guinea in West Africa, hence the name. Originally the guinea had a face value of 20 shillings but fluctuations in the price of gold led the government to fix the face value at 21 shillings (nowadays £1.05 in decimal) from 1717 until it was replaced by the sovereign 100 years later.

Despite the fact that the last actual guinea coin was struck in 1813, the term 'guinea' to represent 21 shillings was used in accounting and on price lists etc right up to the introduction of decimal coins in 1971. In fact, the 'guinea' lives on in horse racing circles and most importantly, it is still used as the denomination of choice when pricing this price guide!

Under the reign of George III guineas and half guineas were struck throughout the reign with very few years omitted. By 1787 they were onto the 5th bust type! The third guinea coin was introduced in 1797 and is therefore covered here in its entirety. During the reign of George III the large 5 guinea and 2 guinea denominations were issued as patterns only. A quarter guinea was also struck in 1762. The 5 guinea, 2 guinea and quarter guinea are outside the current scope of this book.

The guinea was struck with a weight of about 8.2 grammes and just like the sovereign, they are made of 22ct (916.67 parts per 1000) gold. The half guinea is logically 4.1 grammes and the third guinea therefore about 2.7 grammes.

Forgeries are sometimes encountered but it should also be brought to the readers attention that so-called imitation guineas in brass were made in very large numbers by the Victorians for use as gaming counters. Mainly either guinea or half guinea replicas, these were made after the guinea based coins were demonetised and were never intended to deceive. Often they have an altered reverse legend which usually features an abbreviation of the makers company name by way of advertisement. Novices sometimes assume the brass replicas to be the real thing. They are easy to differentiate as they were never as well made as the real thing and, being brass, are very much lighter.

The Third Guinea, approx. 17mm

Date	Notes	F	VF	EF	UNC
1797	1st bust, date in legend	£150	£280	£500	
1798		£150	£280	£500	
1799		£300	£600	£1000	
1800		£150	£280	£500	
1801	Date under crown	£150	£280	£500	
1802		£150	£280	£500	
1803		£150	£280	£500	
1804	2nd bust	£150	£280	£500	
1806		£150	£280	£500	
1808		£150	£280	£500	
1809		£150	£280	£500	
1810		£150	£280	£500	
1811		£300	£800	£1500	
1813		£300	£500	£900	

1803 Third Guinea

1810 Third Guinea

The Half Guinea, approx. 21mm

1797	5th George III bust type	£200	£400	£700
1798		£200	£400	£700
1798	8 struck over a 7	£220	£450	£800
1800		£250	£600	£1200
1801	6th George III bust type	£200	£300	£600
1802		£200	£300	£600
1803		£200	£300	£600
1804	7th George III bust type	£200	£300	£500
1805		Rare		
1806		£200	£350	£600
1808		£200	£350	£600
1809		£200	£350	£600
1810		£200	£350	£550
1811		£350	£500	£900
1813		£300	£400	£700

Earlier 5th bust coins 1787 to 1796 exist. Values tend to be around the same as the 1790s coins above with the exception of 1792, which is considerably scarcer.

The Guinea, approx. 23.5mm

Date	Notes	F	VF	EF	UNC
1797	5th George III bust type	£320	£550	£1000	
1798		£320	£500	£800	
1798	8 struck over a 7	£320	£500	£1000	
1799		£350	£600	£1200	
1813	Military (6th) bust	£600	£1500	£3000	

Earlier 5th bust coins 1787 to 1796 exist. Values tend to be around the same.

1790 Guinea. Reverse enlaged to the right.

Sovereign based denominations 1816 - 1968

An act of parliament was implemented on the 3rd August 1816, stating that new gold coins were to be minted to replace the Guinea and its fractions. The new sovereigns were given a face value of 20 shillings (One pound Sterling) and the half sovereigns were logically worth 10 shillings. The new coins were all struck using machinery installed at the new Tower Hill site, which until a few years previous, had been occupied by tobacco warehouses.

The sovereign, being a new denomination and smaller (the sovereign is just over 22mm, the half sovereign 19.5mm) than the established Guinea, was not popular at first. The government stuck with it and popularity soon grew. Almost 200 years later, the sovereign has established itself as one of the most popular gold coins in the world!

Benedetto Pistrucci came up with idea of having a Saint George motif on the reverse. At that time his artistic reputation had gained him quite a celebrity status and he was commissioned to design the Saint George and the bust of King George III for use on the new coins. As if that wasn't enough, he was also given the task of engraving the dies for the coins too.

Gold, being quite inert, tends to stay bright and for that reason the BU grade is not shown. Gold is heavy too and quite soft, so is more prone to being marked and scratched. Problems with the eye appeal will of course affect the value. At the time of writing (Aug 2012) the price of gold bullion is historically very high. A sovereign is worth £250.00 for its gold content (half that for a half sovereign). Gold prices fluctuate of course, so the internet or a newspaper should be checked for the current rate.

Specifications: All full sovereigns weigh 7.98 grammes and have a diameter of 22.05mm. Half sovereigns weigh 3.99 grammes and have a diameter of 19.5mm. The alloy used for both coins is 916.66 parts per 1000 gold (22 carat) which means that the gold content of an unworn and undamaged sovereign is 7.315 grammes and for a half sovereign 3.658 grammes.

George III

Date	Notes	F	VF	EF	UNC
1817		£250	£330	£440	£700
1818	2nd 8 over 7		£400	£650	£1500
1818		£250	£330	£460	£750
1820	Varieties exist	£300	£330	£500	£750

Rare proofs of 1817 and 1818 exist.

George III 1820 Half Sovereign

* Coins marked with an asterix were struck using a different obverse die. The border, is heavier and an extra tuft of hair can be seen behind the Kings ear.

George IV Laureate Head

Date	Notes	F	VF	EF	UNC
1821	1st Reverse	£500	£1300	£2500	
1821	Proof	Rare			
1823	2nd Reverse	£180	£330	£500	£800
1824		£180	£330	£450	£750
1825		£180	£330	£400	£700
Bare head type from here down.					
1826		£180	£330	£400	£750
1826	*	£180	£330	£350	£700
1826	Proof	Rare			
1827		£170	£300	£500	£750
1827	*	£170	£300	£450	£700
1828		£170	£300	£400	£750
1828	*	£180	£330	£500	£750

William IV

Date	Notes	F	VF	EF	UNC
1831	Plain edge proof	Rare			
1831	Milled edge proof	Rare			
1834		£180	£300	£740	£1250
1835		£200	£320	£640	£1100
1836		£250	£350	£725	£1200
1836	Error, struck using sixpence obv	Rare			
1837		£220	£350	£700	£1200

Victoria - Young Head

Commencing in this reign, gold coins were also minted at colonial mints in Australia, Canada and India. These colonial coins were given mintmarks to distinguish them, whereas London mint coins have no mintmark. The mintmarks used were capital letters. The letters and their positions will be pointed out in the listings. The mint letters and the various slightly different young head busts make this a difficult series to fully understand.

London mint coins with no mintmarks:

Date	Notes	F	VF	EF	UNC
1838		£150	£200	£400	£750
1839	Proof, plain or milled edge	Rare			
1841		£150	£200	£400	£750
1842		£150	£190	£300	£600
1843		£150	£200	£400	£750
1844		£150	£190	£300	£700
1845		£220	£500	£1350	
1846		£150	£190	£350	£700
1847		£150	£190	£350	£700
1848	Tight date	£150	£190	£350	£700
1848	2nd 8 over 7	£220	£350	£500	
1848	Loose date	£160	£220	£400	
1849		£150	£190	£300	£600
1850		£150	£350	£1200	
1851		£150	£190	£300	£600
1852		£150	£200	£300	£600
1853		£150	£200	£300	£600
1853	Proof, large or small dates	Rare			
1855		£140	£200	£300	£600
1856		£140	£200	£300	£600
1856	6 over	£140	£220	£350	£700
1857		£140	£190	£300	£600
1858		£140	£190	£300	£600
1858	Larger 2nd head type	£140	£190	£250	£500
1859		£140	£190	£250	£500
1860		£140	£190	£250	£500
1861		£140	£190	£250	£500
1862		£450	£1500	£4400	
1863		£140	£190	£250	£500

Now with die numbers below the shield

Date	Notes	F	VF	EF	UNC
1863		£140	£220	£350	£600
1864		£140	£180	£280	£500
1865		£140	£180	£280	£500
1866		£140	£180	£280	£500
1867		£140	£180	£280	£500
1869		£140	£180	£280	£500
1870		£140	£170	£280	£500
1870	With re-touched shield legend, coarser teeth.	£160	£300	£800	
1871		£140	£190	£300	£520
1871	With re-touched shield legend, coarser teeth.	£140	£320	£800	
1871	No die number	£250	£500		
1871	Queens' nose points to 'T'	£160	£350	£900	

Victoria 1866 Young head Half Sovereign

Half Sovereign (continued)

Date	Notes	F	VF	EF	UNC
1872	Larger head	£140	£160	£250	£440
1873		£140	£160	£250	£440
1874		£140	£160	£250	£440
1875		£140	£160	£250	£440
1876		£140	£160	£250	£440
1876	Narrow hair ribbon	£170	£300	£460	
1877		£140	£160	£250	£440
1878	Narrow hair ribbon	£160	£300	£460	
1879		£160	£150	£360	£700
1880		£140	£160	£280	£500

No die numbers from this point onwards.

Date	Notes	F	VF	EF	UNC
1880		£140	£150	£250	£440
1883		£140	£150	£250	£440
1884		£140	£150	£250	£440
1885		£140	£150	£250	£440
1885	5 over 3	£150	£250	£350	£730

Sydney mint coins, indicated here by an 'S' after the date and distinguished on the coin by a small 'S' under the shield.

Date	Notes	F	VF	EF	UNC
1871S		£140	£250	£700	£2500
1872S		£140	£250	£700	£2500
1875S		£140	£250	£700	£2500
1879S		£140	£250	£650	£2300
1880S		£140	£250	£650	£2300
1881S		£140	£250	£650	£2300
1882S		£250	£520	£2800	£7000
1882S	Legend close to heavy border (values approximately as above)				
1883S		£140	£250	£600	£3200
1883S	Legend close to heavy border (values approximately as above)				
1886S		£140	£250	£750	£2500
1887S		£140	£250	£750	£2500

Melbourne mint coins, indicated here by an 'M' after the date and distinguished on the coin by a small 'M' under the shield.

Date	Notes	F	VF	EF	UNC
1873M		£140	£250	£680	£2500
1877M		£140	£250	£680	£2500
1877M	Narrow hair ribbon	(values approximately as above)			
1881M		£160	£330	£1350	£4000
1882M	Narrow hair ribbon	£140	£200	£550	£1700
1882M		£140	£200	£550	£1750
1884M		£150	£300	£1450	£4000
1885M		£220	£400	£2000	£5400
1886M		£160	£300	£1500	£3800
1887M		£200	£500	£1900	£5400

Victoria - Jubilee Head

London Mint Coins.

Date	Notes	F	VF	EF	UNC
1887	JEB on truncation	BV	BV	£140	£180
1887	Small close JEB	BV	£140	£190	£300
1887	no JEB	BV	£140	£190	£300
1890	JEB on truncation	£150	£200	£300	
1890	no JEB	BV	BV	£140	£160
1890	*	BV	BV	£140	£160
1891		BV	£140	£170	£250
1891	*	BV	BV	£140	£160
1892	JEB on truncation	£140	£190	£250	
1892	no JEB	BV	£140	£160	£250
1892	*	BV	BV	£140	£200
1893	*	BV	£140	£180	£250

Victoria 1887 Jubilee head Half Sovereign

* Coins marked with an asterix have a lower shield and a slightly spread apart date.

Sydney mint coins, indicated here by an 'S' after the date and distinguished on the coin by a small 'S' under the shield.

1887S	Wide spaced JEB	£140	£190	£300	£1000
1887S	Normal JEB	£140	£190	£300	£1000
1889S		£150	£200	£500	£1800
1891S		£150	£200	£500	£1800
1891S	no JEB	£150	£200	£500	£1800

Melbourne mint coins, indicated here by an 'M' after the date and distinguished on the coin by a small 'M' under the shield.

1887M	Wide spaced JEB	£140	£190	£280	£900
1887M	Close JEB	£140	£190	£280	£900
1893M		£140	£200	£400	£1500

Victoria - Veiled Head

The Pistrucci St George is back for now, and remains in constant use on half sovereigns right up to the present day. London mint coins are dealt with first.

Date	Notes	F	VF	EF	UNC
1893		BV	BV	£140	£160
1893	Proof				£550
1894		BV	BV	£140	£160
1895		BV	BV	£140	£160
1896		BV	BV	£140	£160
1897		BV	BV	£140	£160
1898		BV	BV	£140	£160
1899		BV	BV	£140	£160
1900		BV	BV	£140	£160
1901		BV	BV	£140	£160

Victoria 1896 Veiled head Half Sovereign

Melbourne mint coins, indicated here by an 'M' after the date and distinguished on the coin by a small 'M' on the gound below the horses right rear hoof.

Date	Notes	F	VF	EF	UNC
1893M		Rare			
1896M		£140	£190	£350	£1500
1899M		£140	£190	£350	£1500
1900M		£140	£190	£350	£1500

Perth mint coins, indicated here by a 'P' after the date and distinguished on the coin by a small 'P' on the gound below the horses right rear hoof.

Date	Notes	F	VF	EF	UNC
1899P	Proof		Unique		
1900P		£160	£300	£500	£2000

Sydney mint coins, indicated here by an 'S' after the date and distinguished on the coin by a small 'S' on the gound below the horses right rear hoof.

Date	Notes	F	VF	EF	UNC
1893S		£140	£190	£300	£1100
1897S		£140	£190	£250	£1000
1900S		£140	£190	£250	£1000

Edward VII

London mint coins listed first.

Date	Notes	F	VF	EF	UNC
1902		BV	BV	£140	£160
1902	Matte Proof				£180
1903		BV	BV	£130	£150
1904		BV	BV	£130	£150
1904	No B.P. in exergue BV	BV	£130	£140	
1905		BV	BV	£130	£150
1906		BV	BV	£130	£150
1907		BV	BV	£130	£150
1908		BV	BV	£130	£150
1909		BV	BV	£130	£150
1910		BV	BV	£130	£150

Edward VII 1909 Half Sovereign

Melbourne mint coins, indicated here by an 'M' after the date and distinguished on the coin by a small 'M' on the gound below the horses right rear hoof.

Date	Notes	F	VF	EF	UNC
1906M		£130	£160	£380	£1400
1907M		£130	£160	£200	£400
1908M		£130	£160	£200	£400
1909M		£130	£160	£200	£450

Perth mint coins, indicated here by a 'P' after the date and distinguished on the coin by a small 'P' on the gound below the horses right rear hoof.

Date	Notes	F	VF	EF	UNC
1904P	No B.P. in exergue	£150	£250	£600	£1300
1904P		£140	£200	£600	£1300
1908P		£140	£200	£600	£1300
1909P		£140	£200	£500	£1300

Sydney mint coins, indicated here by an 'S' after the date and distinguished on the coin by a small 'S' on the gound below the horses right rear hoof.

Date	Notes	F	VF	EF	UNC
1902S		BV	£130	£200	£400
1902S	Proof		Rare		
1903S		BV	£130	£250	£300
1906S		BV	£130	£250	£300
1908S		BV	£130	£200	£250
1910S		BV	£130	£190	£250

George V, London mint coins listed first

Date	Notes	F	VF	EF	UNC
1911		BV	BV	£130	£150
1911	Proof				£330
1911	Matte proof	Rare			
1912		BV	BV	£130	£150
1913		BV	BV	£130	£150
1914		BV	BV	£130	£150
1915		BV	BV	£130	£150

George V 1912 Half Sovereign

Melbourne mint coins, indicated here by an 'M' after the date and distinguished on the coin by a small 'M' on the gound below the horses right rear hoof.

Date	Notes	F	VF	EF	UNC
1915M		BV	BV	£130	£150

Perth mint coins, indicated here by a 'P' after the date and distinguished on the coin by a small 'P' on the gound below the horses right rear hoof.

Date	Notes	F	VF	EF	UNC
1911P		BV	£130	£200	£700
1915P		BV	£150	£200	£800
1918P		£190	£350	£550	£900

Sydney mint coins, indicated here by an 'S' after the date and distinguished on the coin by a small 'S' on the gound below the horses right rear hoof.

Date	Notes	F	VF	EF	UNC
1911S		BV	£130	£150	£160
1912S		BV	£130	£150	£160
1914S		BV	BV	£130	£150
1915S		BV	BV	£130	£150
1916S		BV	BV	£130	£150

Pretoria (South Africa) mint coins, indicated here by an 'SA' after the date and distinguished on the coin by a small 'SA' on the gound below the horses right rear hoof.

Date	Notes	F	VF	EF	UNC
1923SA	Proof				£350
1925SA		BV	BV	£130	£160
1926SA		BV	BV	£130	£160

Edward VII

Extremely rare, not to be confused with modern fantasy patterns.

George VI

This issue was a plain edged proof only, struck in London. 5001 were struck, the odd '1' was for the King himself.

1937	Plain edge Proof	£600

Elizabeth II - No half sovereigns issued until 1980.

George III

Date		F	VF	EF	UNC
1817		£500	£600	£1200	£2500
1818		£800	£1200	£1800	£3000
1818	Slanted colon after BRITANNIAR (values approx. as above)				
1818	Wiry curls, normal legend				Rare
1818	Wiry curls, slanted colon as above				Rare
1819		£25k	£40k	£50k	£75k
1820		£400	£500	£1200	£2000

Rare proofs exist of 1817, 1818 and 1820. Varieties of the 1820 coin also exist.

George III 1820 Sovereign

George IV

Date		F	VF	EF	UNC
1821		£450	£650	£1000	£2600
1822		£450	£700	£1000	£2600
1823		£1200	£2500	£4500	£6800
1824		£500	£800	£1200	£3300
1825		£1200	£2500	£4500	£6800

George IV Laureate head 1821 Sovereign

Now using the bare head

Date		F	VF	EF	UNC
1825		£450	£600	£1000	£2300
1826		£450	£600	£1000	£1900
1827		£500	£650	£1500	£2600
1828		£6500	£9500	£15k	£25k
1829		£500	£650	£1600	£2600
1830		£500	£650	£1600	£2600

Rare proofs exist of 1821, 1825 and 1826.

George IV Bare head 1830 Sovereign

William IV

Date		F	VF	EF	UNC
1831		£1000	£2000	£2800	£4500
1831	WW incuse, no stops (values approximately double those shown above)				
1831	Nose points to 2nd I in BRITANNIAR	Fine: £12k	VF: £20k		
1832		£550	£700	£1500	£2400
1832	Nose points to 2nd I in BRITANNIAR	Fine: £800	VF: £1500		
1833		£550	£800	£1800	£3500
1835		£550	£850	£2000	£3500
1836		£550	£800	£1800	£3500
1836	N of ANNO in shield	£5k	£8k	£15k	
1837		£500	£700	£1400	£2200
1837	3 over 8	£600	£1000	£2000	

Rare proofs exist of 1830, 1831 and 1832.

William IV 1831 Sovereign

Victoria

The first coins listed here are all the shield reverse type, from the London mint. Rare proofs exist for 1838 and 1839.

Date	Notes	F	VF	EF	UNC
1838		£900	£1300	£2000	£3300
1839		£1000	£1500	£2500	£6000
1841		£4k	£6k	£8k	£15k
1842		£280	£300	£450	£2000
1842	Open 2	£330	£400	£700	£2500
1843		£280	£400	£600	£2000
1843	2nd 3 over 2	£400	£800	£2000	£3500
1843	Narrow Shield	£4k	£6k	£8k	£15k
1844	Large 44	£300	£400	£600	£2000
1844	Smaller 44	£300	£400	£1000	£2500
1844	date over inverted 4	Rare			
1845		£280	£350	£450	£1000
1845	date over inverted 4	Rare			
1845	I for 1 in date	£600	£1200		
1846		£280	£350	£450	£1000
1846	date over inverted 4	Rare			
1846	I for 1 in date	£600	£1200		
1847		£280	£350	£450	£1000
1847	I for 1 in date	Rare			
1848		£1500	£2500	£3500	£15k
1848	2nd larger head	£350	£400	£650	£3500
1849		£350	£400	£650	£3500
1849	I for 1 in date	£400	£600	£1000	
1850		£300	£400	£600	£1800
1850	I for 1 in date	£300	£500	£1000	
1851		£280	£350	£350	£850
1852		£220	£280	£350	£850
1852	I for 1 in date	£300	£500	£1000	
1853		£270	£290	£350	£850
1853	WW incuse	£300	£400	£1000	£2500
1854		£350	£500	£2000	£3500
1854	WW incuse	£270	£290	£350	£850
1855		£300	£400	£1000	£2500
1855	WW incuse	£270	£290	£350	£850
1856		£280	£300	£450	£850
1857		£270	£290	£450	£850
1858		£300	£400	£700	£1500
1859		£270	£290	£450	£850
1859	Additional line on ribbon	£850	£1750	£3500	
1860		£270	£290	£450	£850
1860	large O	£270	£290	£450	£900
1861		£270	£290	£300	£750
1861	I for 1 in date	£350	£500	£1000	

Victoria - Young Head, shield reverse

A complicated issue with mint letter, lots of varieties and two entirely different reverses. The first coins listed here are all the shield reverse type, from the London mint.

Date	Notes	F	VF	EF	UNC
1862	Wide date	£270	£330	£450	£850
1862	Narrow date	£270	£330	£500	£900
1863		£270	£300	£300	£750
1863	Roman I for 1	£320	£500	£1000	
1863	'827' on truncation		Rare		
Die numbers below wreath until 1874					
1863		£270	£250	£300	£750
1863	'827' on truncation, no die No.	Rare			
1864		£270	£290	£300	£850
1865		£280	£310	£400	£850
1866		£270	£300	£300	£650
1866	2nd 6 over 5	£280	£310	£450	£800
1868		£300	£330	£500	£850
1869		£270	£300	£350	£550
1870		£270	£300	£400	£650
1870	WW incuse	£280	£310	£450	£850
1871		£270	£300	£350	£450
1872		£270	£300	£350	£450
1872	No die number (earlier bust)	£270	£300	£380	£550
1873		£270	£300	£380	£550
1874		£1000	£1850	£2500	£5000

Victoria Young head, shield back 1852 Sovereign

Melbourne mint coins, indicated here by an 'M' after the date and distinguished on the coin by a small 'M' under the wreath.

Date	Notes	F	VF	EF	UNC
1872M		£210	£249	£300	£600
1872M	2 over 1	£250	£400	£850	£2000
1874M		£210	£240	£400	£800
1880M		£350	£750	£1750	£3500
1881M		£220	£289	£400	£1200
1882M		£190	£240	£320	£600
1883M		£220	£400	£850	£1750
1884M		£210	£230	£300	£500
1885M		£210	£230	£300	£500
1886M		£700	£2500	£4500	£8000
1887M		£500	£1250	£3250	£6000

The image below shows the die number location on a shield back Victorian sovereign. The number '101' is shown here, but the die numbers do range from very low numbers to 3 digit figures.

They were used in order to log and gain some idea of the speed with which the dies became worn. Interestingly, when the young head Victorian sovereign dies were considered not good enough for use with sovereigns, the obverses were used to strike the obverses of the pre 1860 copper farthings.

Victoria Young head, shield back 1871 Sovereign

Victoria - Young Head, shield reverse

Sydney mint coins, indicated here by an 'S' after the date and distinguished on the coin by a small 'S' under the wreath.

Date	Notes	F	VF	EF	UNC
1871S		£260	£290	£350	£550
1871S	WW incuse	£260	£300	£370	£650
1872S		£260	£300	£350	£650
1873S		£260	£290	£340	£600
1875S		£260	£290	£340	£500
1877S		£260	£290	£340	£500
1878S		£260	£290	£340	£500
1879S		£260	£290	£340	£500
1880S		£260	£290	£340	£600
1881S		£260	£290	£340	£600
1882S		£260	£290	£320	£550
1883S		£260	£290	£320	£550
1884S		£260	£290	£320	£500
1885S		£260	£290	£320	£500
1886S		£260	£290	£320	£500
1887S		£260	£300	£450	£700

Victoria - Young Head, St George reverse

A change back to the St George reverse now, which is still used today. The shield back coins were produced simultaneously, but were mainly struck in the colonies. London mint coins are listed first.

Date	Notes	F	VF	EF	UNC
1871		BV	£260	£300	£350
1871	Longer horse tail, smaller B.P (approximately the same as above)				
1871	Proof				£5000
1872		BV	£260	£300	£350
1873		BV	£260	£300	£350
1874		BV	£260	£320	£400
1876		BV	£260	£300	£350
1878		BV	£260	£300	£350
1879		£300	£750	£1500	
1880		BV	£260	£300	£350
1880	Short horse tail	BV	£260	£300	£350
1880	no B.P	BV	£260	£300	£400
1880	2nd 8 over 7	£260	£290	£300	£450
1880	2nd 8 over 7, no B.P	£260	£300	£400	£500
1880	Longer horse tail	BV	£260	£300	£350
1884		BV	£260	£300	£350
1885		BV	£260	£300	£350

Victoria - Young Head, St George reverse

Melbourne mint coins, indicated here by an 'M' after the date and distinguished on the coin by a small 'M' under the bust of Queen Victoria.

Date	Notes	F	VF	EF	UNC
1872M		£270	£360	£800	£3000
1873M		BV	£260	£320	£800
1874M		BV	£260	£320	£800
1875M		BV	£260	£320	£700
1876M		BV	£260	£320	£700
1877M		BV	£260	£320	£700
1878M		BV	£260	£300	£600
1879M		BV	£260	£290	£600
1880M		BV	£260	£290	£600
1881M		BV	£260	£290	£600
1881M	No B.P	BV	£260	£290	£600
1882M	No B.P	BV	£260	£290	£600
1882M		BV	£260	£290	£600
1882M	Broader truncation	BV	£260	£290	£600
1883M		BV	£260	£290	£600
1883M	Broader truncation	BV	£260	£290	£600
1884M		BV	£260	£290	£600
1884M	No B.P	£260	£290	£400	
1884M	Broader truncation	BV	£260	£290	£500
1885M		BV	£260	£290	£500
1885M	Broader truncation	BV	£260	£290	£500
1886M		BV	£260	£290	£500
1887M		BV	£270	£300	£600

Victoria Young head, St. George reverse 1879 Melbourne mint Sovereign

The red spot in the image above shows the location of the mint letter when it is present under the bust of Queen Victoria.

Victoria - Young Head, St George reverse

Sydney mint coins, indicated here by an 'S' after the date and distinguished on the coin by a small 'S' under the bust of Queen Victoria.

Date	Notes	F	VF	EF	UNC
1871S	Short horse tail	£260	£300	£500	£1600
1871S	Long horse tail	BV	£280	£400	£1200
1872S		BV	£260	£300	£800
1873S		BV	£260	£320	£900
1874S		BV	£260	£290	£900
1875S		BV	£260	£200	£900
1876S		BV	£260	£290	£750
1879S		£260	£300	£800	£2500
1880S	Long horse tail	BV	£260	£300	£800
1880S	W.W complete	BV	£260	£300	£700
1880S	No B.P	BV	£260	£300	£550
1881S	W.W wide spaced and short (values approximately as above)??				
1881S	W.W complete	BV	£260	£320	£600
1882S	No B.P	BV	£260	£320	£400
1882S		BV	£260	£320	£600
1883S		BV	£260	£300	£1000
1884S		BV	£260	£300	£500
1885S		BV	£260	£300	£500
1886S		BV	£260	£300	£500
1887S		BV	£260	£300	£500

Victoria Young head, St. George reverse 1887 Sydney mint Sovereign

Victoria - Jubilee Head, St George reverse
London mint coins first.

Date	Notes	F	VF	EF	UNC
1887		BV	£260	£290	£360
1887	Proof				£800
1888		BV	£260	£290	£350
1888	D:G: closer to crown	BV	£260	£290	£340
1889		BV	£260	£290	£340
1890		BV	£260	£290	£340
1891	Short horse tail	£270	£320	£800	
1891	Longer horse tail	BV	£260	£290	£320
1892		BV	£260	£290	£320

Victoria Jubilee head 1893
Sydney mint Sovereign

Melbourne mint coins, indicated here by an 'M' after the date and distinguished on the coin by a small 'M' under the horses rear right hoof.

Date	Notes	F	VF	EF	UNC
1887M		BV	£260	£290	£330
1887M	Small spaced J E B	BV	£270	£300	£350
1888M		BV	£260	£290	£330
1889M		BV	£260	£290	£330
1890M		BV	£260	£290	£330
1891M		BV	£260	£290	£330
1892M		BV	£260	£290	£330
1893M		BV	£260	£290	£320

Sydney mint coins, indicated here by an 'S' after the date and distinguished on the coin by a small 'S' under the horses rear right hoof.

Date	Notes	F	VF	EF	UNC
1887S		BV	£290	£500	£1600
1887S	Proof	Rare			
1888S	Small spaced J E B	BV	£270	£300	£360
1889S		BV	£270	£300	£350
1890S		BV	£270	£300	£350
1891S		BV	£270	£300	£350
1892S		BV	£270	£300	£350
1893S		BV	£270	£300	£350

Victoria - Widow Head, St George reverse
London mint coins first.

Date	Notes	Fine	VF	EF	UNC
1893		BV	BV	£270	£320
1893	Proof				£550
1894		BV	BV	£260	£300
1895		BV	BV	£260	£300
1896		BV	BV	£260	£300
1898		BV	BV	£260	£300
1899		BV	BV	£260	£300
1900		BV	BV	£260	£300
1901		BV	BV	£260	£300

Victoria Veiled head
1900 Sovereign

Melbourne mint coins, indicated here by an 'M' after the date and distinguished on the coin by a small 'M' under the horses rear right hoof.

Date	Notes	Fine	VF	EF	UNC
1893M		BV	BV	£270	£300
1894M		BV	BV	£270	£300
1895M		BV	BV	£270	£300
1896M		BV	BV	£270	£300
1897M		BV	BV	£270	£300
1898M		BV	BV	£270	£300
1899M		BV	BV	£260	£300
1900M		BV	BV	£260	£300
1901M		BV	BV	£260	£300

Sydney mint coins, indicated here by an 'S' after the date and distinguished on the coin by a small 'S' under the horses rear right hoof.

Date	Notes	Fine	VF	EF	UNC
1893S		BV	BV	£270	£300
1894S		BV	BV	£270	£300
1895S		BV	BV	£270	£300
1896S		BV	BV	£280	£300
1897S		BV	BV	£270	£300
1898S		BV	BV	£270	£300
1899S		BV	BV	£270	£300
1900S		BV	BV	£270	£300
1901S		BV	BV	£270	£300

Perth mint coins, indicated here by an 'P' after the date and distinguished on the coin by a small 'P' under the horses rear right hoof.

Date	Notes	Fine	VF	EF	UNC
1899P		£300	£350	£500	£1200
1900P		BV	BV	£260	£300
1901P		BV	BV	£260	£300

Edward VII
London mint coins first.

Date	Notes	F	VF	EF	UNC
1902	Matte Proof				£280
1902		BV	BV	£270	£300
1903		BV	BV	£260	£300
1904		BV	BV	£260	£300
1905		BV	BV	£260	£300
1906		BV	BV	£260	£300
1907		BV	BV	£260	£300
1908		BV	BV	£260	£300
1909		BV	BV	£260	£300
1910		BV	BV	£260	£300

Edward VII 1902 Sovereign

Ottawa (Canada) mint coins, indicated here by a 'C' after the date and distinguished on the coin by a small 'C' under the horses rear right hoof.

Date	Notes	F	VF	EF	UNC
1908C	Proof				£4000
1909C		BV	£260	£320	£550
1910C		BV	£280	£330	£450

Melbourne mint coins, indicated here by an 'M' after the date and distinguished on the coin by a small 'M' under the horses rear right hoof.

Date	Notes	F	VF	EF	UNC
1902M		BV	BV	£270	£320
1903M		BV	BV	£260	£300
1904M		BV	BV	£260	£300
1905M		BV	BV	£260	£300
1906M		BV	BV	£260	£300
1907M		BV	BV	£260	£300
1908M		BV	BV	£260	£300
1909M		BV	BV	£260	£300
1910M		BV	BV	£260	£300

Above: The enlarged reverse area of a 1902 Sovereign. The red spot shows the location (if present) of the mint letter on St. George reverse sovereigns and half sovereigns from the Jubilee Victoria type to the last colonial mint sovereigns during the reign of George V.

Perth mint coins, indicated here by an 'P' after the date and distinguished on the coin by a small 'P' under the horses rear right hoof.

Date	Notes	F	VF	EF	UNC
1902P		BV	BV	£260	£300
1903P		BV	BV	£260	£300
1904P		BV	BV	£260	£300
1905P		BV	BV	£260	£300
1906P		BV	BV	£260	£300
1907P		BV	BV	£260	£300
1908P		BV	BV	£260	£300
1909P		BV	BV	£260	£300
1910P		BV	BV	£260	£300

Edward VII

Sydney mint coins, indicated here by an 'S' after the date and distinguished on the coin by a small 'S' under the horses rear right hoof.

Date	Notes	F	VF	EF	UNC
1902S		BV	BV	£270	£300
1903S		BV	BV	£270	£300
1904S		BV	BV	£270	£310
1905S		BV	BV	£270	£300
1906S		BV	BV	£270	£300
1907S		BV	BV	£270	£300
1908S		BV	BV	£270	£300
1909S		BV	BV	£270	£300
1910S		BV	BV	£270	£300

George V - London mint coins first

Date	Notes	F	VF	EF	UNC
1911		BV	BV	£260	£300
1911	Proof				£500
1912		BV	BV	£260	£300
1913		BV	BV	£260	£300
1914		BV	BV	£260	£300
1915		BV	BV	£260	£300
1916		BV	BV	£270	£310
1917			£1500	£5000	£10000
1925		BV	BV	£210	£220

George V 1914 Sovereign

Ottawa (Canada) mint coins, indicated here by a 'C' after the date and distinguished on the coin by a small 'C' under the horses rear right hoof.

Date	Notes	F	VF	EF	UNC
1911C		BV	BV	£280	£320
1913C		£350	£700	£1400	
1914C		£300	£450	£800	
1916C		£2000	£4000	£8000	
1917C		BV	£260	£290	£350
1918C		BV	£260	£290	£350
1919C		BV	£260	£290	£350

Bombay (India) mint coins, indicated here by an 'I' after the date and distinguished on the coin by a small 'I' under the horses rear right hoof.

Date	Notes	F	VF	EF	UNC
1918I		BV	BV	£260	£290

Melbourne mint coins, indicated here by an 'M' after the date and distinguished on the coin by a small 'M' under the horses rear right hoof.

Date	Notes	F	VF	EF	UNC
1911M		BV	BV	£260	£300
1912M		BV	BV	£260	£300
1913M		BV	BV	£260	£300
1914M		BV	BV	£260	£300
1915M		BV	BV	£260	£300

George V

Date	Notes	F	VF	EF	UNC
1916M		BV	BV	£260	£300
1917M		BV	BV	£260	£300
1918M		BV	BV	£260	£300
1919M		BV	£260	£290	£350
1920M		£750	£1500	£3000	
1921M		Rare			
1922M		Rare			
1923M		BV	£260	£290	£350
1924M		BV	£280	£320	£400
1925M		BV	BV	£260	£300
1926M		BV	£270	£300	£400
1928M		Rare			
1929M		£600	£1000		
1930M		BV	£260	£290	£350
1931M		£270	£300	£300	£550

Perth mint coins, indicated here by a 'P' after the date and distinguished on the coin by a small 'P' under the horses rear right hoof.

Date	Notes	F	VF	EF	UNC
1911P		BV	BV	£260	£300
1912P		BV	BV	£260	£300
1913P		BV	BV	£260	£300
1914P		BV	BV	£260	£300
1915P		BV	BV	£260	£300
1916P		BV	BV	£270	£300
1917P		BV	BV	£260	£300
1918P		BV	BV	£270	£300
1919P		BV	BV	£270	£300
1920P		BV	BV	£270	£300
1921P		BV	BV	£270	£300
1922P		BV	BV	£270	£300
1923P		BV	BV	£270	£300
1924P		£280	£300	£360	£400
1925P		£300	£400	£1000	£1500
1926P		£300	£400	£1000	£1500
1927P		£260	£290	£380	£500
1928P		BV	£220	£300	£350
1929P		BV	BV	£280	£320
1930P		BV	BV	£280	£320
1931P		BV	BV	£280	£320

Sydney mint coins, indicated here by an 'S' after the date and distinguished on the coin by a small 'S' under the horses rear right hoof.

Date	Notes	F	VF	EF	UNC
1911S		BV	BV	£260	£300
1912S		BV	BV	£260	£300
1913S		BV	BV	£260	£300
1914S		BV	BV	£270	£300
1915S		BV	BV	£260	£300
1916S		BV	BV	£270	£300

George V

Date	Notes	F	VF	EF	UNC
1917S		BV	BV	£270	£300
1918S		BV	BV	£270	£300
1919S		BV	BV	£270	£300
1920S		Rare			
1921S		£450	£800	£1200	£1800
1922S		£3000	£5000		
1923S		£3000	£5000		
1924S		£450	£650	£850	£1350
1925S		BV	BV	£260	£300
1926S		£5000	£10000		

Pretoria (South Africa) mint coins, indicated by an 'SA' after the date and distinguished by a small 'SA' under the horses rear right hoof.

Date	Notes	F	VF	EF	UNC
1923SA		£1000	£2000		
1923SA	Proof				£750
1924SA		£1500	£3500		
1925SA		BV	BV	£260	£300
1926SA		BV	BV	£260	£300
1927SA		BV	BV	£260	£300
1928SA		BV	BV	£260	£300
1929SA		BV	BV	£260	£300
1930SA		BV	BV	£260	£300
1931SA		BV	BV	£260	£300
1932SA		BV	BV	£270	£300

George V 1931 Pretoria mint (SA) Sovereign

Edward VIII

Extremely rare, not to be confused with modern fantasy patterns.

George VI

This issue was a plain edged proof only, struck in London. 5001 were struck, the odd '1' was for the King himself.

Date	Notes	F	VF	EF	UNC
1937	Plain edge Proof				£1500

George VI 1937 Proof and Elizabeth II first bust Sovereign obverses.

Elizabeth II

Date	Notes	F	VF	EF	UNC
1957		BV	BV	BV	£260
1958		BV	BV	BV	£260
1959		BV	BV	£260	£270
1962		BV	BV	BV	£260
1963		BV	BV	BV	£260
1964		BV	BV	BV	£260
1965		BV	BV	BV	£260
1966		BV	BV	BV	£260
1967		BV	BV	BV	£260
1968		BV	BV	BV	£260
(Decimal 1974 to 1982*)		BV	BV	BV	£260

*Coins were not struck every year.

George III

Date	Notes	F	VF	EF	UNC
1820	Pattern / Proof only	Rare			

George IV

Date	Notes	F	VF	EF	UNC
1823	St. George reverse		£850	£1500	£3000
1826	Proof (illustrated)				£4000

Other dates/proofs all very rare

George IV 1825 Proof Two Pound Coin

William IV

Date	Notes	F	VF	EF	UNC
1831	Proof				£4000

Victoria

Date	Notes	F	VF	EF	UNC
1887	Jubilee Head	£550	£640	£700	£800
1887	Jubilee Head Proof				£1000
1893	Veiled Head	£550	£650	£760	£1000
1893	Veiled Head Proof				£1500

Edward VII

Date	Notes	F	VF	EF	UNC
1902		£550	£650	£700	£800
1902	Proof				£700

George V

Date	Notes	F	VF	EF	UNC
1911	Proof				£800

Edward VII

Not issued.

George VI

Date	Notes	F	VF	EF	UNC
1937	Proof				£650

Elizabeth II

None until 1980.

George VI 1937 Proof Two Pound Coin

George III

Date	Notes	F	VF	EF	UNC
1820	Pattern/Proof only	Rare			

George IV

Date	Notes	F	VF	EF	UNC
1826	Patten/Proof only				£10000

William IV

Not issued.

Victoria

Date	Notes	F	VF	EF	UNC
1839	Young head, proof only				£25000+
1887	Jubilee Head	£1350	£1500	£1600	£1700
1887	Jubilee Head Proof				£2800
1893	Veiled Head	£1350	£1500	£1700	£2500
1893	Veiled Head Proof				£3750

Edward VII

Date	Notes	F	VF	EF	UNC
1902		£1350	£1500	£1600	£1700
1902	Proof				£1800

George V

Date	Notes	F	VF	EF	UNC
1911	Proof				£2100

Edward VIII

Not issued.

George VI

Date	Notes	F	VF	EF	UNC
1937	Proof				£1700

Elizabeth II

None until 1980.

Victoria 1887 Five Pound Coin

George V 1911 Proof
Five Pound Coin obverse

Coins not intended for circulation - Proof and Uncirculated Sets

Prices quoted are for sets in well preserved cases of issue.

1826	Farthing - £5 coin	(11 coins)	Very Rare	£35,000+
1826	As above with 4 maundy coins.		Very Rare	£35,000+
1831	Farthing - £2 coin	(14 coins)	Very Rare	£35,000+
1839	Farthing - £5 coin	(15 coins)	Very Rare	£60,000+
1853	Half Farthing to 5s	(16 coins)	Very Rare	£50,000+
1887	3d to £5 coin. Jubilee head	(11 coins)	Very Rare	£12,500+
1887	3d to Crown	(7 coins)	Rare	£2,000+
1893	3d to £5 coin	(10 coins)	Very Rare	£12,500+
1893	3d to Crown	(6 coins)	Rare	£2,000+
1902	Maundy 1d - £5 coin	(13 coins)	Scarce (matte)	£5,000
1902	Maundy 1d - Sovereign	(11 coins)	Scarce	£1,500
1911	Maundy 1d - £5 coin	(13)	Scarce	£6,500
1911	Maundy 1d - Sovereign	(11 coins)	Scarce	£1,500
1911	Maundy 1d - Half Crown	(8 coins)	Scarce	£800
1927	3d to Crown	(6 coins)	Scarce	£550
1937	Half Sovereign - £5	(4 coins)	Rare	£5,000
1937	Farthing - Crown & Maundy	(15 coins)	Common	£300
1950	Farthing - Half Crown	(9 coins)	Scarce	£180
1951	Farthing - Crown	(10 coins)	Scarce	£200
1953	Farthing - Crown	(10 coins)	Scarce	£900
1953	Farthing - Half Crown	(9 uncirculated coins)	Common	£20
1968/71	Blue folder 'last decimal set'		Very Common	£0.50
1970	Half Penny - Halfcrown	(8 coins)	Very Common	£25

Complete Maundy Sets (1, 2, 3 and Fourpence coins)

Date	ESC	VF	EF	UNC/BU
GEORGE III .925 fine silver.				
4 coins of 12mm, 14mm, 18mm and 19.5mm				
1800	2421	£60	£150	£300/
Coins now smaller:11mm, 13mm, 16mm and 18mm				
1817	2422	£80	£150	£300/
1818	2423	£80	£150	£300/
1820	2424	£80	£150	£300/
GEORGE IV .925 fine silver.				
4 coins of 11mm, 13mm, 16mm and 18mm				
1822	2425	£80	£150	£250/
1822	2426	Proof set		/£600
1823	2427	£80	£150	£250/
1824	2428	£80	£150	£300/
1825	2429	£70	£120	£250/
1826	2430	£70	£120	£250/
1827	2431	£70	£150	£300/
1828	2432	£70	£120	£250/
1828	2433	Proof set		/£750
1829	2434	£70	£120	£250/
1830	2435	£70	£150	£300/
WILLIAM IV .925 fine silver.				
4 coins of 11mm, 13mm, 16mm and 18mm				
1831	2436	£70	£150	£175/
1831	2437	Proof set		£350/£450
1831	2438	Proofs in gold		/£15,000
1832	2439	£70	£150	£250/
1833	2440	£70	£150	£250/
1834	2441	£70	£150	£250/
1835	2442	£70	£150	£250/
1836	2443	£75	£150	£250/
1837	2444	£75	£150	£250/
VICTORIA Young Head .925 fine silver.				
4 coins of 11mm, 13mm, 16mm and 18mm				
1838	2445		£200	£350/
1838	2446	Proof set		£300/
1838	2447	Proofs in gold		/£15,000
1839	2448		£150	£300/

Date	ESC		EF	UNC/BU
VICTORIA (continued)				
1839	2449	Proof set		£300/
1840	2450		£200	£300/
1841	2451		£200	£300/
1842	2452		£200	£300/
1843	2453		£200	£300/
1844	2454		£200	£300/
1845	2455		£200	£300/
1846	2456		£200	£300/
1847	2457		£200	£300/
1848	2458		£200	£300/
1849	2459		£200	£300/
1850	2460		£200	£300/
1851	2461		£200	£300/
1852	2462		£200	£300/
1853	2463		£200	£300/
1853	2464	Proof set		£400/£500
1854	2465		£150	£400/
1855	2466		£150	£400/
1856	2467		£150	£400/
1857	2468		£150	£400/
1858	2469		£150	£400/
1859	2470		£150	£400/
1860	2471		£150	£400/
1861	2472		£150	£400/
1862	2473		£150	£400/
1863	2474		£150	£400/
1864	2475		£150	£400/
1865	2476		£150	£400/
1866	2477		£150	£400/
1867	2478		£150	£400/
1867	2479	Proof set		£265/
1868	2480		£150	£400/
1869	2481		£150	£400/
1870	2482		£140	£400/
1871	2483		£140	£250/
1871	2484	Proof set		£500/
1872	2485		£140	£250/
1873	2486		£140	£250/
1874	2487		£140	£250/
1875	2488		£140	£250/
1876	2489		£140	£250/
1877	2490		£140	£250/
1878	2491		£140	£250/
1878	2492	Proofs	£300	£400/

Date	ESC	EF	UNC/BU
VICTORIA (continued)			
Young Head .925 fine silver.			
4 coins of 11mm, 13mm, 16mm and 18mm			
1879	2493	£100	£250/
1879	ND Proofs		£1,000
1880	2494	£100	£250/
1881	2495	£100	£250/
1881	2495A Proofs		£300+/
1882	2496	£100	£250/
1883	2497	£100	£250/
1884	2498	£100	£250/
1885	2499	£100	£250/
1886	2500	£100	£250/
1887	2501	£110	£200/
Jubilee Head			
1888	2502	£100	£150/
1888	2503 Proofs	?	?
1889	2504	£100	£150/
1890	2505	£100	£150/
1891	2506	£100	£150/
1892	2507	£100	£150/
Old/Widow Head			
1893	2508	£80	£100/
1894	2509	£80	£100/
1895	2510	£80	£100/
1896	2511	£80	£100/
1897	2512	£80	£100/
1898	2513	£90	£125/
1899	2514	£90	£125/
1900	2515	£90	£120/
1901	2516	£80	£100/
EDWARD VII types the same.			
1902	2517	£80	£100/
1902	2518 Matt Proofs		/£120
1903	2519	£80	£100/
1904	2520	£80	£120/
1905	2521	£80	£120/
1906	2522	£80	£120/
1907	2523	£80	£120/
1908	2524	£80	£120/
1909	2525	£90	£150/
1910	2526	£90	£150/
GEORGE V types as Edward VII, .500 silver from 1921.			
1911	2527	£80	£100/
1911	2528 Proof set		/£100

Date	ESC	EF	UNC/BU
GEORGE V (continued)			
1912	2529	£80	£100/£120
1913	2530	£80	£100/£120
1914	2531	£80	£100/£120
1915	2532	£80	£100/£120
1916	2533	£80	£100/£120
1917	2534	£80	£100/£120
1918	2535	£80	£100/£120
1919	2536	£80	£100/£120
1920	2537	£80	£100/£120
1921	2538	£80	£100/£120
1922	2539	£85	£100/£125
1923	2540	£80	£100/£120
1924	2541	£80	£100/£120
1925	2542	£80	£100/£120
1926	2543	£80	£100/£120
1927	2544	£80	£100/£120
1928	2545	£80	£100/£120
1929	2546	£80	£100/£120
1930	2547	£80	£100/£120
1931	2548	£80	£100/£120
1932	2549	£80	£100/£120
1933	2550	£80	£100/£120
1934	2551	£80	£100/£120
1935	2552	£80	£100/£120
1936	2553	£80	£100/£125
GEORGE VI types as above, .500 silver.			
1937	2554		£90/£120
1938	2555		£90/£120
1939	2556		£90/£120
1940	2557		£90/£120
1941	2558		£90/£120
1942	2559		£90/£120
1943	2560		£90/£120
1944	2561		£90/£120
1945	2562		£90/£120
1946	2563		£90/£120
Silver reverted to .925 Fine.			
1947	2564		£90/£120
1948	2565		£90/£120
1949	2566		£90/£120
1950	2567		£90/£120
1951	2568		£90/£120
1952	2569		£90/£120

Original documentation adds value. Add £10 - £15 for a set housed in contemporary dated case.

Date	ESC		UNC/BU
ELIZABETH II .925 fine silver. 4 coins of 11mm, 13mm, 16mm & 18mm			
1953	1,025		£400/£600
1953	In gold	(1985)	£5,750
1954			£100/£120
1955			£100/£120
1956			£100/£120
1957			£100/£120
1958			£100/£125
1959			£100/£120
1960			£100/£120
1961			£100/£130
1962			£100/£120
1963			£100/£120
1964			£100/£120
1965			£100/£120
1966			£100/£125
1967			£100/£125
1968			£100/£125
1969			£100/£125
1970			£100/£120
Now Decimal pence.			
1971			£100/£120
1972			£100/£120
1973			£100/£120
1974			£100/£120
1975			£100/£120
1976			£100/£120
1977			£100/£120
1978			£100/£120
1979			£100/£120
1980			£100/£120
1981			£100/£120
1982			£100/£120
1933			£100/£120
1984			£100/£120
1985			£100/£120
1986			£100/£120
1987			£100/£120
1988			£100/£120
1989			£100/£120
1990			£100/£120
1991			£100/£120
1992			£100/£120
1993			£100/£120
1994			£120/£125
1995			£120/£125
1996			£120/£125
1997			£120/£135
1998			£120/£135
1999			£120/£135
2000			£120/£135
2001			/£140
2002			/£140
2003			/£140
2004 - 2010			£200/£300

Left: George III 1800 maundy set. The last set before the current sizes were adopted in 1817. Below: 1882 Victoria maundy set. The reverse types have remained very similar ever since.

Victoria 1898 Maundy Groat

Maundy obverses usually use the same bust as the circulation coinage. With the exception that the laureate George IV bust was used for all George IV maundy money and the first Elizabeth II bust has been, and is still being used for all Elizabeth II maundy money.

Maundy Singles

It's generally preferred to collect complete maundy sets rather than try to obtain each date individually, mainly because individual coins can be difficult to track down of certain dates, and it can often work out more expensive. Also, complete sets tend to all have the same toning, and they therefore match better. Individual coins do often appear for sale with prices varying greatly. Below is a list of approximate prices for coins in Uncirculated condition:

George III	UNC
1800 set	
Fourpence	£50 - £100
Threepence	£50 - £100
Twopence	£40 - £80
Penny	£30 - £70
1817 - 1820 type	
Fourpence	£30 - £40
Threepence	£30 - £40
Twopence	£20 - £30
Penny	£20 - £30
George IV	
Fourpence	£20 - £40
Threepence 1822	£40 - £50
Threepence (others)	£20 - £30
Twopence	£15 - £25
Penny	£15 - £25
William IV	
Fourpence	£20 - £30
Threepence	£30 - £40
Twopence	£20 - £30
Penny	£15 - £25
Victoria	
Young Head (1838 - 1887)	
Fourpence	£20 - £30
Threepence	£35 - £40
Twopence	£15 - £20
Penny	£10 - £20

Victoria (continued)	UNC
Jubilee Head (1888 - 1892)	
Fourpence	£15 - £25
Threepence	£20 - £30
Twopence	£10 - £20
Penny	£10 - £20
Old Head (1893 - 1901)	
Fourpence	£15 - £25
Threepence	£20 - £30
Twopence	£10 - £20
Penny	£10 - £20
Edward VII & George V	
Fourpence	Around £15
Threepence	£15 - £20
Twopence	£10 - £15
Penny	£10 - £15
George VI and Elizabeth II up to 1970 except 1953 coins, which are expensive	
Fourpence	Around £20
Threepence	Around £20
Twopence	Around £20
Penny	Around £20
Elizabeth II 1971 - 2000	
Fourpence	Around £30
Threepence	Around £30
Twopence	Around £30
Penny	Around £30

More recent maundy sets/singles are not often offered.

A Glossary Numismatic terms and Abbreviations

Many of the abbreviations used in this book are standard Coin collectors jargon, there are however, a few that may not be so obvious. This glossary should clear things up:

Alignment: The relationship between the obverse and reverse of the coin. Either the reverse is up side down compared to the obverse when rotated with fingers at the top and bottom of the coin, or the reverse is up the same way when the coin is rotated with fingers at the top and bottom of the coin. The latter is the most common alignment for British coins dated 1860-date and may be referred to in this book as up/up. In the same way the upside down alignment may sometimes be referred to as up/down.

Berries: Usually refers to the number of berries in the wreath around the monarch's head.

BV: Bullion Value. i.e no collectors premium over the value of the metal.

H: An 'H' after the date in the first column indicates the coin was struck at the Heaton Mint in Birmingham. The 'H' mintmark will appear on the coin either next to, or under its date.

Incuse: Struck inwards. Lettering or a design element on a coin that is the opposite to raised. For example, the edge lettering on the modern £1 coin.

KN: A 'KN' after the date in the first column indicates the coin was struck at the Kings Norton Mint in Birmingham. The 'KN' will appear on the coin next to the date.

Modified Effigy: (George V only) In the absence of a direct comparison, the modified effigy (or modified head) can be distinguished by the initials which appear on the truncation of the neck. Before modification, the initials B.M. are placed near the centre of truncation. After modification they appear, without stops, well to the right thus: BM (not B.M.) The initials are those of the designer of the coin: Bertram Mackennal.

Mule: A Mule is when a coin gets made with the wrong combination of obverse and reverse.

Obverse: (or Obv) The side of the coin with the head of the Monarch on.

Pattern: A proposed coin type that was not used for circulation.

Piedfort: A coin that is struck on a thicker blank than is usual. Relatively recently the Royal mint starting coining Silver Piedfort coins.

Pointing/Points: To distinguish a different die used to strike a particular coin, often 'pointings' are used. They normally refer to a letter or design element on the coin, and to whether it points directly at, or between two border teeth or another element of the coin.

Proof: A special striking of a coin using specially prepared and polished dies and blanks.

Reverse: (or Rev) The opposite side of the coin to the obverse, or the 'tails' side.

Teeth / Beads: The small teeth or circles surrounding the inner rim of many British coins. Beads are circular, teeth are elongated.

Truncation: (or trunc) The base of the monarch's neck, often containing the designers initials.

The following books were used as reference during the writing of this book, and are recommended for further reading:

Previous editions of **"Collectors' Coins Great Britain"**. (most are out of print)

"The British Bronze Penny", by Michael Gouby.
(Available from the author: www.michaelcoins.co.uk)

"English Copper, Tin and Bronze coins in the British Museum 1558-1958", by C Wilson Peck. (out of print)

"The Bronze Coinage of Great Britain", by Michael J Freeman. (Available new)

"English Silver Coinage since 1649", by P Alan Rayner. (Available new)

"British Silver Coins Since 1816", by Peter J Davies. (Available new)

"Standard Catalog of World Coins", by C L Krause and C Mishler. (Available new, published in the USA)

"A Guide Book of English Coins", by K E Bressett. (Out of print but often available second hand on eBay, published in the USA)

"The Sovereign", by Daniel Fearon / Brian Reeds. (Available new)

"The Identification of British 20th Century Bronze Coin Varieties", by D J Groom. (Available new)

"The Identification of British 20th Century Silver Coin Varieties", by D J Groom. (Available new)

Also recommended is: **"The Early British Bronze Bun Penny 1860 - 1865 and their varieties",** by John Jerrams.

The Cover Coin

The main image on the front of this book is of an 1847 Gothic Crown. Strictly a proof coin only, but with a fairly high mintage for a proof of 8,000. Very highly regarded and certainly one of the most attractive British coins of all time. This is one of those coins that should only be purchased from reputable dealers as quite a few (assumed Chinese) forgeries have been brought to my attention over the last year or so.

Copyright Notice